VOLUME 9

FUNK & WAGNALLS WILDLIFE ENCYCLOPEDIA

GENERAL EDITORS • Dr. Maurice Burton and Robert Burton

Also published as The International Wildlife Encyclopedia and Encyclopedia of Animal Life.

Funk & Wagnalls, Inc., New York, New York

Harpy eagle

The harpy eagle of Central and South America is the largest of all eagles. The female, which is one third as large as the male, weighs 16 or 17 lb. The wings are short and very broad compared with the longer and narrower wings of soaring birds of prey such as the golden eagle and the condor. The tail is long and square and the legs are strong, the feet being as large as a man's hand. The powerful bill is deep and has a very large hook. In short, the harpy eagle is a most impressive bird, made all the more so by the crown of long plumes reminiscent of those of the crowned eagle (p 587). The plumage is black on the back and chest and white underneath. The head and neck are light grey with a black crest. The tail is olive-brown with three black bars. Immature birds are lighter.

Harpy eagles range from southern Mexico to Colombia and on the eastern side of the Andes from Venezuela to northern Argentina. A second species is the New Guinea harpy eagle **Harpyopsis novaeguineae** whose wing and tail feathers are highly prized as ornaments by the local tribesmen.

Eagles of the forest

Harpy eagles are not particularly rare, but not much is known about them. This is because travel is difficult in these regions, which often have hardly been penetrated by Europeans. Even where the eagles' homes are quite easily reached the thick forest makes study difficult. Until 1960 our knowledge of the harpy eagle was limited mainly to anecdotal observations by 19th-century explorers. Then two harpy eagle nests were discovered in Guyana by J Fowler and J Cope. These were watched closely for 6 months from a hide nearby and an adult female and two young eagles were captured alive and tamed. From the results of these observations some idea of the habits of harpy eagles has been pieced together.

Another reason for the harpy eagle being so difficult to study is that it hunts among the trees and is rarely seen above the tree canopy except when it leaves the foliage to fly up to its nest in the top of a very tall tree. At this height it is difficult to find a vantage point from which to watch activities at the nest.

Catching monkeys

With their broad wings and long tail harpy eagles can flit through the dense growth with an amazing speed and agility—speeds of 40–50 mph have been recorded. As they fly from tree to tree they listen and watch for signs of their prey, which consists mainly of monkeys, such as capuchins, and sloths which they probably catch in the same way as the crowned eagle. Remains around the nests observed in Guyana showed that the harpy eagles were catching agoutis, porcupines, opossums and coatis as well

Zool Soc London

Crowned in splendour: the largest of all eagles, a harpy looks over its shoulder with a fixed stare. It is extremely difficult to study in its South American home; it lives in the thick tropical forests and as it hunts in the forest canopy, it is rarely seen above the trees.

993

the parents. As the parent approached the calling increased and became continuous as the parent arrived. Food was dropped in the nest and the young eagle drove its parent away from it.

The young harpy eagles obviously spend a long time near the nest before fending for themselves, so it is probable that harpy eagles breed only every other year.

Trial and error

The two young harpy eagles were probably in the process of being left to fend for themselves. Their parents were bringing food only at long intervals, and when food was brought the young eagles resented their parents' presence near it. Soon they would have to hunt for themselves and this would probably begin by their parents leaving them to starve so necessity would force them to learn. Until then, the eagles appeared unwilling to fly although they took a keen interest in animals about them, and were especially excited by monkeys or parrots. Food offered by the observers on the ground was ignored but a chicken placed in the next tree was immediately taken, so it seems there was some unwillingness to move far.

It was also noticed that when a young eagle took food from its parent it repeatedly crushed it with its talons, as if 'killing' it. So two parts of hunting behaviour were instinctive. The eagles seemed to know what was food, judging from their interest in animals that came within the vicinity of the nest, and they appeared to know how to kill it, but apparently they have to learn how to catch it. The mock killing is also interesting because it is often seen in captive animals. When given their food they will throw it about and pounce on it or even chase an imaginary object. It seems that the sequence of behaviour has to be carried out even when artificial conditions have eliminated the need for some of its stages.

class	**Aves**
order	**Falconiformes**
family	**Accipitridae**
genus & species	*Harpia harpyja*

Victim hunting: with broad wings and long tail a harpy eagle can flit through the dense growth with amazing speed and agility—speeds of 40—50 mph have been recorded. As they fly from tree to tree they listen and watch for signs of prey—the victims are capuchin monkeys, sloths, porcupines, agoutis, parrots and macaws.

as monkeys and sloths. The presence of agoutis in the prey showed that harpy eagles sometimes hunt near the ground. Parrots and macaws also feature in the eagle's diet but there were no remains of these found at the two nests observed by Fowler and Cope. Considering the wide range of the harpy eagles, however, it would be unwise to base an inventory of their diet on observations at two neighbouring nests.

The captive eagles ate ½ lb of food per day and it is calculated from this that in the wild they would need to kill twice a week.

Nesting in the treetops

Harpies nest in forks of tall trees such as mahogany or silk-cotton trees 200 ft high,

not at the very top but in a fork just above the surrounding canopy. The nest is made of stout sticks, up to 2½ in. thick, interwoven to form a platform 4 ft across and 2 ft thick. It is built up over successive years.

The two nests were watched late in the season, so nothing is known of the courtship and incubation periods. Probably only one egg is laid. The young eagles studied had left the nests and were living among the branches within 100 yd. They spent most of their time perching on boughs, retiring to the shade in the heat of the day. When hungry they perched in an exposed position and called at intervals. At each call they flapped their wings, displaying white plumage underneath. This is thought to be a visual signal which, with the calls, attracts

Harpy eagle
(Harpia harpyja)

Harrier

Harriers are a group of hawks characteristically living in open country which they scan for prey, flying low over the ground. Their plumage is usually brown, but the males of some species have some grey in it, and the black harrier of South Africa and the pied harrier of Eastern Asia are largely black. Harriers have rather owl-like heads, long wings and long legs. They are found throughout the world where there is open country, except in polar regions, on the Galapagos Islands and the islands of the southwest Pacific. The hen harrier— so called because it harried domestic hens in the days when it was abundant and chickens roamed free around farmyards— breeds in temperate regions around the world, including most of Europe. In North America, where it ranges from California to Alaska, the hen harrier is called the marsh hawk. This name is rather unfortunate as another European species is called the marsh harrier. This is the largest European species, with broader wings and slower flight than the others. It breeds from the south of Finland southwards to North Africa and across Asia, also in Australia, New Zealand, Madagascar and neighbouring small islands. The African marsh harrier is another species, living in the southern half of Africa. It is often found in large groups.

The breadwinner returns: a marsh harrier lands with food for her chicks.

Regurgitation of food for hungry chicks to peck from the beak tip.

Communal roosts

Harriers have been persecuted over the centuries by gamekeepers and others, but in recent years there have been signs of a recovery in the numbers of some species. Destruction of habitat and poisoning by toxic chemicals have, however, acted against harriers as they have against so many other birds of prey. The European marsh harrier lives in reedbeds and swamps, habitats that are becoming increasingly more rare. It is also susceptible to human disturbance and in 1966 the total British breeding population was about six pairs, half of which were in the Royal Society for the Protection of Birds reserve at Minsmere in Suffolk. The hen harrier, on the other hand, has increased in numbers since the Second World War left many areas without gamekeepers. Forestry plantations have also given it a safe refuge.

Outside the breeding season harriers are gregarious. There is general migration southwards in winter and harriers can be seen moving in flocks. The pallid harrier becomes one of the commonest birds of prey on the plains of Africa and Asia during the winter and it joins Montagu's harrier to form communal roosts of up to 200 birds. The swamp harrier of Australia, New Zealand and New Guinea forms similar concentrations. Unlike other birds of prey, harriers roost and nest on the ground.

Pouncing on their prey

Harriers search for their prey by quartering the ground, flying low then dropping into the grass or reeds. The animals taken depend very much on the location. The swamp harrier of New Zealand and Australia used to live mainly on rabbits before most of them were wiped out by myxomatosis, and the marsh harrier eats large numbers of frogs. In Africa harriers often live on the flocks of migrating locusts.

Although they may concentrate on some prey animals, harriers are omnivorous. They very rarely capture birds in the air but often catch young birds on the ground or steal eggs from nests. Marsh harriers take chicks of game and poultry, especially in Spain and North Africa where chickens are smaller than in more northern parts of Europe. They also take marsh birds such as gallinules and coots, and in Africa they feed on rats and mice. A hen harrier was once seen to attack a duck sitting on the water. It eventually managed to pick the duck up but it was too heavy and had to be dropped.

Spectacular show-offs

Harriers have spectacular courtship displays. The male climbs to heights of 200 ft or so and dives with wings closed, sometimes spinning round, then soars up again. Often it loops the loop or flies upside down, or dives at the female who turns on her side to fend him off with her feet.

The nests are built on the ground, sometimes in small colonies of 15—20 pairs. On swampy ground a hummock is chosen and the nest built from dead grasses or rushes. The marsh harrier builds a fairly bulky nest clear of possible flooding. Some 3—5 eggs are laid and incubated by the female alone for about 1 month. The male feeds the female during this time but rarely comes near the nest. As he approaches he calls to the female who leaves the nest and flies out to him. He drops the food for her to catch in mid-air or else she will take it from his talons. At other times both will land at the second nest near the main nest.

After the chicks hatch they are brooded continuously for 9—10 days. Later they leave the nest and shelter in the surrounding vegetation, coming back to be brooded at night or in heavy rain. They start to fly when 5—6 weeks old and stay with their parents for another 2—3 weeks.

At the beginning of the breeding season harriers are very shy and will abandon their nests if disturbed. Later, when the chicks have hatched, they become aggressive and swoop on intruders. This is used in catching them. A model owl is put on a post near the harrier's nest with a fine, strong net behind it. The harriers dive-bomb the owl and end up in the net.

Favoured by man

Looking up information on predatory animals is a heart-breaking business. In nearly every case their numbers are decreasing through destruction of their habitats or because they have been slaughtered as vermin. Birds of prey make the worst reading, for in Europe they were beginning to make a comeback because of protection and the decrease of game preserves. Then in the late 1950s their numbers began to slump again, this time because pesticides picked up in their food seem to be making them sterile.

It is very pleasing, then, to find a case where man's activities have actually helped a species. In the case of the swamp harriers in New Zealand this has not been intentional. Thousands were killed annually but it is one of the few native birds of New Zealand that has been favoured by European settlement. The woodlands have been cut down to make sheep pasturage, giving the harrier a larger area in which to hunt, and introduced rodents and rabbits have supplied extra food.

class	**Aves**
order	**Falconiformes**
family	**Accipitridae**
genus & species	***Circus aeruginosus*** *marsh harrier* ***C. approximans*** *swamp harrier* ***C. cyaneus*** *hen harrier* ***C. pygargus*** *Montagu's harrier* *others*

Hartebeest

The hartebeest is a large ungainly-looking antelope standing 4−5½ ft at the shoulder, the coat being some shade of brown, the limbs often blackish or plum-coloured. The back slopes sharply from the shoulders to the hindquarters. The head is narrow and elongated, with a long face and narrow muzzle, and a high bony base for the horns, which vary much in shape. Seen from the front they may form a V or a U or they may be curly-bracket shaped, with the tips pointing backwards.

These curious antelopes, among the commonest in Africa, used at one time to be spread over the whole of the continent. There are three species. The common hartebeest ranges across Central Africa from Guinea to Ethiopia. Lichtenstein's hartebeest from Tanzania and Zambia to Mozambique. The Cape or red hartebeest was once found from the Zambesi and Southwest Africa to the Cape of Good Hope. In the common hartebeest the colour is a more or less uniform brown with only a trace of darkening on the limbs. In Lichtenstein's it is more contrasted, with darkening on the lower parts of the limbs and a yellow patch on the rump. In the red hartebeest the colour is much richer, the whole of the limbs being blackish as well as the shoulders and haunches, the rump and underside being white. In the common hartebeest the hairs of the face are mostly directed forward; in the other two, they are directed backward. Again, in the red and Lichtenstein's hartebeests the forehead is broader and the horns more bent back and down than in the common. On the other hand Lichtenstein's hartebeest has an unusually short, broad horn base. The red hartebeest is rather isolated from the other two, but the ranges of Lichtenstein's and the common hartebeest meet in Tanzania without interbreeding taking place.

Playing at statues

Hartebeest live in small herds of up to 15, in well established territories. The territory is bounded by natural features, such as hills or streams. A typical one studied by Dieter Backhaus was 1 sq mile in extent. The range is restricted in the main to well-watered areas so there is no problem about finding drinking water. Hartebeest begin to move around sunrise and seek food on the higher slopes of their territory. The male, of which there is only one in the herd, marks his territory not by glandular secretions (for the facial glands are poorly developed) but by what is called 'static-optical demarcation'. That is, he stands still on a high point, such as a termite-mound, where neighbouring herd males can see him.

When a strange male intrudes, the resident male chases the newcomer, galloping very fast and overtaking him. Some yards ahead, the resident male makes a quick turn, halts and threatens the other with his horns.

MJ Coe

△ Patient hartebeest mother suckles her young.   ▽ Termite-mound statue: male surveys territory.

JS Wightman

997

The intruder gallops on, the defender follows and repeats the manoeuvre until the intruder is out of his territory. There are reports of quite fierce fighting between males, even ending fatally, but these have not been confirmed. Females and youngsters sometimes spar with one another in play. Hartebeest run with a stiff-legged gait. The herd maintains a rigid rank order; the dominant animal is always the adult male. When he is temporarily away, as in the breeding season, the top-ranking female takes over leadership. The ranking is expressed in the order in which the herd follow trails and flee from danger. The young are either in the rear, or else near the top female. The trails become quite well-marked and criss-cross the territory; the herd travels back and forth for 1–3 miles daily, breaking rank when it stops to feed, and reforming when on the move again.

Hartebeest quite commonly wallow; they push the head and horns into the mud and rub them against the flanks. There is generally a salt-lick somewhere in the territory, which is constantly visited.

Watchful feeding

Hartebeest feed on the open plains, occasionally wandering into woodland areas. Nearly all their food is grass. The animal nibbles away until its mouth is full, then raises its head and chews while looking around for enemies.

In the breeding season, from mid-April to mid-May, the male leaves the rest of the herd until the females are ready to mate, after which he leaves again for a short while. A female's breeding condition lasts only a single day. The young are born 8 months later, at the turn of the year. They do not at first follow the herd but lie still on the ground, the male constantly keeping watch.

Keeping an eye on the foe

The chief enemy is the lion. When alarmed hartebeests stand on small mounds or termite hills for a better view. When the foe has been identified the herd flees for 200–500 yd. If the enemy has disappeared, the animals are liable to return to locate it again. They tend to flee in zigzag fashion, although the young flee in a straight line. Backhaus suggests that this enables them to keep alternate eyes on the predator, whereas if they kept just one eye on it they would tend to run in a circle.

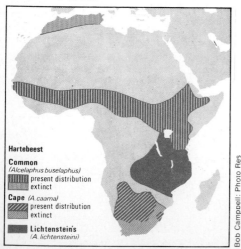

Hartebeest

Common
(Alcelaphus buselaphus)
present distribution
extinct

Cape (A. caama)
present distribution
extinct

Lichtenstein's
(A. lichtensteini)

Bob Campbell: Photo Res

998

Jane Burton: Photo Res

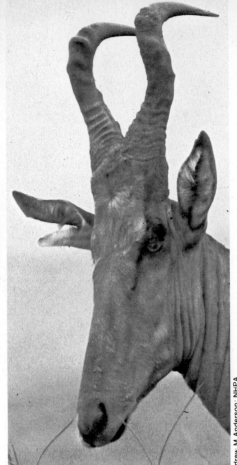

Andrew M Anderson: NHPA

Hartebeest live in small herds of up to 15 in well-established territories (above). Hills or streams and other natural features, such as the termite mound seen on the previous page, act as boundaries. A hartebeest is easily identified by its characteristic head gear (right): the narrow and elongated head has a long face and narrow muzzle and a high bony base for the horns. The horns, although similar in thickness and ring marks, may vary very much in shape—seen by studying all the hartebeest photographs. Entanglement for power (left): fierce fights occur between males for herd dominance and territorial rights. Below: Feeding by Lake Albert.

Peter Hill

Pure and impure races

In 1929 a paper by AE Ruxton and Ernst Schwarz demonstrated quite clearly the trend of evolution in hartebeests. Spreading out from East Africa their range (as traced by the physical characters of the different races of common hartebeest) spread north through Ethiopia into North Africa, down the west coast of Africa and across via Nigeria and the southern Sudan into East Africa again. The Sudan race interbreeds with the old, long-standing forms of Kenya and Ethiopia, and in some places, especially in the Rift Valley of East Africa, the populations are extraordinarily variable. Clearly there are many hybrids formed from the neighbouring races: the old Kenya race has bracket-shaped horns, the 'new' Sudan race has horns forming a V when seen from the front; in the Rift Valley horns of every conceivable intermediate shape are found, yet on either side of the Valley the parent races are quite uniform. This remarkable demonstration of hybridisation stands as a classic in the field of mammalian systematics.

Although the range of hartebeest must at one time have been continuous all around the Sahara it is not continuous now, partly through extermination by man, partly through climatic and environmental change. The Shari River system of the Lake Chad district separates two races, while the spread of the Sahara desert cuts off the North African hartebeests from the others.

The North African hartebeest, a small race, has never been very common in modern times. The last one in Tunisia was killed in 1902 at Bir-Kecira; in 1925, three were killed in the Missour region of south east Morocco. G Seurat in 1943 considered that a few still might linger in the valleys of Chott Tigri in Morocco, but these suppositions are unconfirmed; the race may well be extinct there.

Elsewhere in Africa, hartebeest of all three species are abundant. The red hartebeest, however, is almost extinct within the borders of South Africa proper, although it is still found in good numbers in Southwest Africa, Botswana and Angola. The last remnant in South Africa, about 30 in number, were collected by Mr Hans Moe on his farm in Natal during the last war, and protected. The farm was sold some years later, on Mr Moe's retirement, to Dr A Seele. The Natal Parks Board tried to remove the remaining six—reduced to that number by a cold winter and by poaching—to a game sanctuary in 1952, but they simply refused to be corralled!

class	**Mammalia**
order	**Artiodactyla**
family	**Bovidae**
genus & species	***Alcelaphus buselaphus*** common hartebeest **A. caama** Cape or red hartebeest **A. lichtensteini** Lichtenstein's hartebeest

999

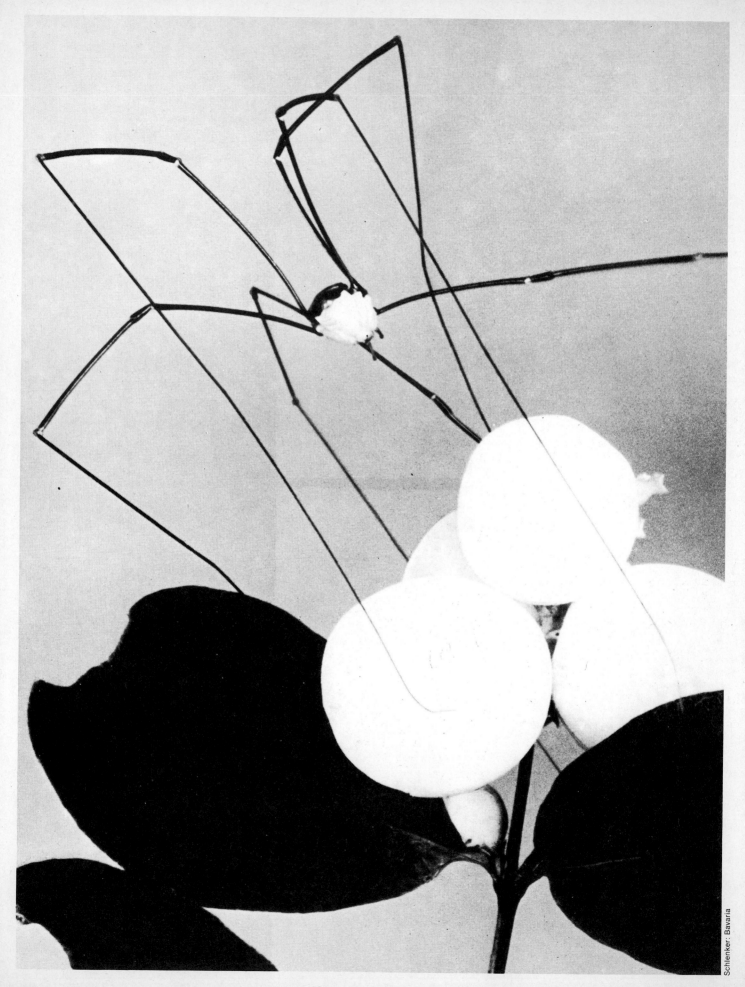

Harvester

*Although often called harvest spiders, harvesters or harvestmen are not true spiders but belong to a separate order, the Opiliones. Both belong, however, to the same class, the Arachnida. Harvesters differ from spiders in several important respects. They have only two eyes, 'back to back', on turrets on the thorax, whereas spiders have at least eight eyes arranged in a group on the head. In addition, while all spiders have the abdomen sharply marked off from the thorax, harvesters have no such 'waist'. Unlike spiders, harvesters never spin webs. Other differences are in their habits. Generally speaking, male and female harvesters are difficult to tell apart except that the male usually has longer legs and a smaller body. In some species, however, notably in the common **Phalangium opilio**, the pedipalps (mouth parts) of the male are long, to give the impression of another pair of legs. The 2 000 species of harvester are distributed all over the world except for the polar regions. Only 21 are found in Britain.*

In the United States harvesters are known as daddy long-legs, a name sometimes used for them in Britain but which is more properly applied to the cranefly (p 601).

Losing valuable legs

Mainly drab and inconspicuous, harvesters are nevertheless familiar to most people. They live in woods and among long grass and other low-growing vegetation but being largely nocturnal we more often see them under flowerpots and beneath window sills. The gardener turning over a pile of rubbish or compost, or perhaps an old sack lying on the ground, may see one of the larger species scuttling away on its long, thread-like legs. Sometimes in making its escape one of its legs is lost. The leg is thrown off at a breaking point between the first two joints. After coming away the leg may twitch and quiver for some seconds. Harvesters appear to suffer little inconvenience from the loss, but cannot regenerate a lost limb. This is a further point of difference from spiders which are able to regrow all of their legs at once if need be. Harvesters have been found still moving around with only two legs. The second pair of legs, usually the longest, carry sense organs. They are used to feel the way over obstacles or, held in the air, to detect vibrations. They seem also to carry a sense of taste or smell. Loss of this pair of legs slows a harvester down very considerably.

◁ *Snowberry ballet: a harvestman delicately feels its way over the snowberry bush, searching for victims which it can catch in its beak-like jaws, piercing the prey to suck out its juices.*

▷ *Hitch-hikers all aboard! Red mites are often found on harvesters as passengers taking rides from one place to another.*

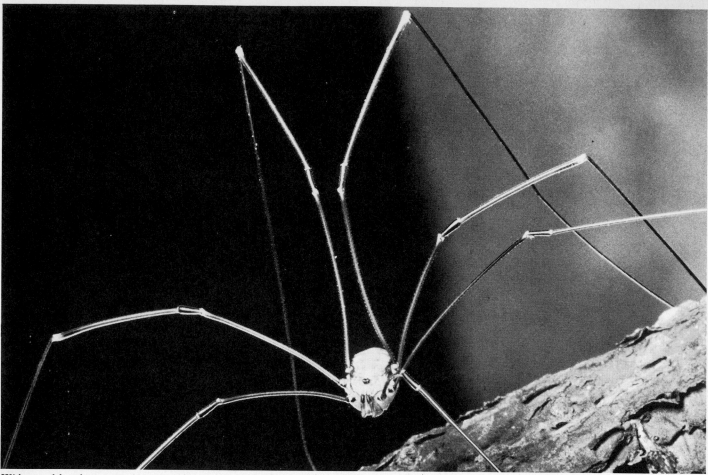

Widespread legs have earned the harvester the name daddy long-legs. They often wave their sensitive legs in the air which has given rise to the old bit of folklore which claims a farmer can tell where his cows are by watching a harvester's legs and seeing in which direction they point.

Feeding on scraps

Harvesters are largely carnivorous, feeding on a variety of small invertebrates, such as insects, spiders and mites. They do not inject poison into their victims, as spiders do. Instead, they have large and powerful beak-like jaws, or chelicerae, with which to pierce the prey and suck out its juices and soft tissues. They also eat some of the more juicy forms of plant life. They are in fact omnivorous. In captivity they can be fed on almost anything edible, from bread and milk to meat; this is probably the reason why they are so common in garden rubbish heaps. If a bottle containing scraps of meat and fat is placed with its opening level with the soil and left overnight, this will often contain one or more harvesters in the morning. Harvesters also need to drink at frequent intervals to keep in good condition. They cannot endure the long periods of starvation that spiders can and lack of water for drinking soon makes them stiff and torpid. A drink, however, quickly restores them.

Three months of life

Mating is by internal fertilisation and there is no courtship. Matings are frequent, the same male mating several times in rapid succession with the same partner or with other females. The female lays her eggs, which are less than $\frac{1}{25}$ in. diameter, in the soil or in crevices in the bark of trees, usually in late summer or autumn using an ovipositor. In some species, the eggs overwinter, young harvesters being hatched the following year. In others, the eggs hatch fairly quickly but the young hibernate through the winter. Apart from size, there is little or no difference between adult and young harvesters. In some species, males are exceedingly rare and reproduction is largely by parthenogenesis. This is especially true of *Megabunus diadema,* found on mountains in Britain. It is silver, green and black. One count showed only one male to over 400 females.

Growth is by ecdysis, or moulting, the whole skin being shed. There may be seven or eight such skin changes during a harvester's lifetime, with about ten days between each, the moult usually taking place at night. The gossamer-light sloughs, complete in every detail, intact down to the thinnest portions of each leg, may sometimes be found attached to low growing vegetation to which the harvester usually anchors itself for the moult. The old skin splits and the body is drawn out from it. Then each long leg must be removed from its old casing. For this the harvester uses its jaws.

Anaesthetic defence-measure

Harvesters are preyed upon by centipedes and the larger spiders, as well as being taken by the smaller insectivorous birds. Their only defence is to cast a limb which may twitch and wriggle like a living thing, so catching the attention of the predator long enough for the harvester itself to make good its escape, or to discharge an offensive, volatile fluid from glands near the eyes. This fluid seems to affect even harvesters themselves if a group of them are placed in a closed container. They seem to be anaesthetised by it, but if taken out and exposed once more to the air they quickly recover.

Too clean for safety

Having so many sense organs on its legs a harvester must keep them cleared of dust and dirt, so its toilet is carried out with great care. Always after feeding and at other times as well each leg in turn is held in the jaws and slowly pulled through them. By the time this is finished the leg has curved almost into a circle. Then comes the need for cleaning the jaws themselves, and for this the harvester must go to water, rest the front pair of feet on the surface film and dip its face in the water. Sometimes the feet break through the surface film and the animal cannot regain its balance and is drowned. Water for harvesters is a dire necessity for drinking and washing, and also a natural hazard.

phylum	**Arthropoda**
class	**Arachnida**
order	**Opiliones**
family	**Phalangidae**
genera & species	*Phalangium opilio* *Megabunus diadema*

Harvesting ant

*Harvesting ants have the habit of collect-ing seeds of grasses and cereals and storing them in quantity in their under-ground nests. In southern Europe, Asia and Africa they are represented by **Messor**, **Pheidole** and other genera, while in sub-tropical North America ants of the genera **Pogonomyrmex** and **Ischnomyrmex** have adopted a similar mode of life.*

The division into castes is carried to extremes in these ants. The ordinary workers are quite small and normally proportioned, but there are also larger workers and 'soldiers' (largest of all) in which the jaws are much enlarged and the heads proportionally enormous, to accom-modate huge jaw muscles.

Harvesting ants are found in the drier regions of the subtropics and some of them live in deserts.

Village-like colonies

The nest of colonies of harvesting ants is large, sometimes a mound 20 or 30 ft across and penetrating 6 ft or more into the ground, and the entrance is often surround-ed by a crater-like wall of coarse soil par-ticles. The ants forage in large companies and their tracks leading to the nest look like well-marked roads. Within the nest there are special chambers in which the grain is stored.

The seeds are collected from living grasses and from standing crops of grain, or from the ground where it is scattered by primitive harvesting methods. In the Mediterranean and Near East they collect wheat, in Asia millet. The small workers gather the seeds and bring them home, where the husk or chaff is removed by the large workers, and possibly the soldiers, using their powerful jaws, and they also crush the seeds when they are needed as food. Crushed and masti-cated grain is given to the growing larvae and the adult ants also live on the store during times of drought when the foragers can find nothing edible outside the nest. The discarded chaff is thrown outside on a rubbish heap which comes to form a ring round the nest, and is a clearly visible feature of a flourishing colony.

Well-kept granaries

Within the nest the storage chambers are kept carefully drained so the seed remains dry and does not germinate. Also, if the seeds begin to germinate the ants bite off the embryonic root or radicle, so preventing growth. When heavy rain does penetrate to the storage chambers the damp seed is brought to the surface and spread out around the nest to dry as soon as the sun shines. The quality of the seed as food is improved by this treatment, as the starch in the seeds is partly converted to sugar, just as when grain is malted for spirit making.

Accidental crops

When the ants fail to prevent germination they bring the sprouting grain to the surface and throw it on the 'rubbish heap', where

Grace Thompson: Photo Res

*Collect with caution: harvesting ants of the **Pogonomyrmex** have powers of stinging that are almost unequalled among ants. A single sting on the ankle may nearly incapacitate a man for some minutes.*

some of the seeds may germinate successfully and produce plants. It was once thought that the ants deliberately cultivated around their nests the plants that feed them, but in fact such 'sowing' of seed is purely accidental. On the other hand this accidental growth is clearly beneficial to the ants as it creates food plantations.

The life cycle of the harvesters has no particular feature distinguishing it from that of the other ants. Eggs are laid by the queen or queens and the larvae are tended and fed by the workers, passing through a pupal stage before reaching maturity. New colonies are founded by winged queens, each of which breaks off her wings after mating and seeks out a crevice in which to lay eggs and raise the small brood of workers which are the earliest inhabitants of almost every nest of ants.

History and legend

'Go to the ant thou sluggard; consider her ways and be wise: which having no guide, overseer or ruler, provideth her meat in the summer and gathereth her food in the harvest'.

These three verses from the Proverbs of Solomon are evidence that the habits of the harvesting ants made a profound impression upon the early inhabitants of the eastern Mediterranean countries. The observation that ants work industriously without being led or driven by any visible authority shows that the people of the time observed them closely.

Interest in these ants was not, however, purely philosophical. When nests were dug up the considerable quantity of grain in them was well worth gathering in those days of laborious manual agriculture. Appeals to tribal law were sometimes made for their possession, and in some communities the point was resolved by ordaining that grain from the nest must be distributed to the poor.

By an obvious extension from the activities of the harvesting ants a legend arose in the time of the Ancient Greeks of a kind of ant 'not so large as a dog but bigger than a fox', which lived in the deserts of Arabia and mined gold. Expeditions were sent out to locate the ants and capture their treasure, but there is no record of success.

From the other side of the world comes a curious story, based on the industry of the American harvesting ants. Originating in the mythology of the Mayas of Mexico, and recorded by one of the Spanish colonists of the 16th century, it tells of a grain-harvesting ant that planted seeds from which, after long and indirect growth processes, both mankind and his surrounding world were developed. Perhaps this story can be regarded as a very early and primitive forerunner of the idea of evolution.

△ *Harvester ants* **Messor barbarus** *carry grass seeds into their nest. These African ants have a similar mode of life to the other harvesting ants of Eurasia and America.*
▽ *A scientist looks at a sectioned nest of the Argentinian leaf cutter, showing the chambers containing the fungus gardens. Such a colony could contain from 175 000 to 600 000 individuals. From the mound the ants make well-worn paths through the surrounding vegetation and cut large pieces out of leaves and carry them like banners to their nests. The pieces are then cut into smaller fragments and built up on floors of the nest chambers in the form of sponge-like masses, which become covered with a white mould-like fungus mycelium (right).*

class	**Insecta**
order	**Hymenoptera**
family	**Formicidae**
subfamily	**Myrmicinae**
genera	***Messor, Pheidole, Pogonomyrmex, Ischnomyrmex***

Harvest mouse

Except for the pygmy shrew this is the smallest mammal in the British Isles. The harvest mouse also ranges across Europe except for the Mediterranean region, Siberia and China to Formosa. There is another harvest mouse in North America but this belongs to a different family, and it was given the same name only because it resembles the Old World species in size and habits.

The harvest mouse is about 5 in. long of which nearly half is a scaly, almost naked tail. It weighs no more than ¼ oz. Its fur is soft and thick, yellowish-red with white underparts. It has a blunt nose, black, medium-sized eyes, large rounded ears, and a tail prehensile in its outer part.

'Look, no hands' . . . a harvest mouse surveys the scene from the upper storeys of a reedmace, securely anchored by its hind feet alone.

John Markham

Tight-rope walker

The harvest mouse lives in the rank herbage of ditches, pastures and fields of cereal crops, and it sometimes lives in salt marshes, reed beds and dykes. During its waking periods a harvest mouse spends most of its time climbing about the stalks of cereals or other stout plants. Although once thought to be mainly active by day, it is now known to have a 3-hourly rhythm of alternately feeding and sleeping throughout each 24 hours. Every third hour, night and day, it feeds for half an hour and $1\frac{1}{2}-2$ hours of every 3 hours is spent sleeping. Its sleeping nest is a mass of grass blades shredded lengthwise on the ground or in a shallow burrow.

Docile, inoffensive and without any disagreeable odour, the harvest mouse is now less numerous over parts of its range, due, it is thought, to modern agricultural methods such as the use of reaping machines and earlier harvesting.

The most noticeable feature of a harvest mouse is its agile climbing in which the tail plays a large part. The moment the harvest mouse stops moving among vegetation the end of its tail curls around a stalk. While the mouse is moving the tail is constantly taking a partial grip, ready to take a firm

◁ *That divided feeling . . . but the prehensile tail provides security in the rear.*
▽ *A quick sniff at a poppy-head.*

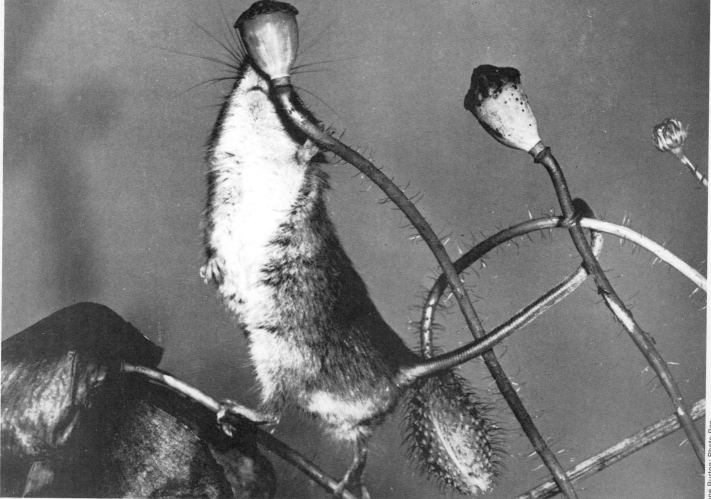

grip when necessary. The mouse can also grip with its hindfeet. The outer of the five toes on each hindfoot is large and opposable to the rest. A harvest mouse can grip a stem with each hindfoot and take hold with its tail, so leaving the front paws free for feeding. It can also use the tail for balance. It will run up a stem that bends under its weight swinging the tail from side to side, looking very much like a tight-rope walker with his long pole.

Choice of cereals

The harvest mouse does not hibernate but winters in burrows in the ground. It will also tunnel into hayricks or cornricks, but these are going out of use in modern agriculture. Its food is a variety of seeds, especially of grasses, and grain. In summer it eats a certain amount of insects.

Nest woven from grasses

The breeding season is from April to September. The female makes a round nest 3 in. in diameter, woven of grass or wheat blades split lengthwise and slung between 2 or 3 stalks. It has no definite entrance, the material being pushed aside for entrance or exit. The male is not allowed into the nest. After a gestation period of 21 days a litter of 5–9 is born. A female may have several litters in a season. The babies open their eyes at 8 days, make their first excursions from the nest at 11 days and are independent at 15 days. Until the end of the year

the juveniles resemble the house mouse in colour. They then take on a reddish tint which begins on the hindquarters and gradually extends forwards. The natural expectation of life is about 1½ years, but 5 years has been reached in captivity. Little is known of enemies but it is safe to assume that harvest mice are killed by small carnivores as well as birds of prey.

American harvest mouse

The Old World harvest mouse belongs to the family Muridae, the American harvest mouse to the family Cricetidae; so it is related to voles. Both are about the same size, both are good climbers and the details of their life history are alike except that the baby American harvest mice open their eyes at 5 days and leave the mother at 10 days. The American species does not have a prehensile tail and its nest is lodged in a shrub well above ground.

Passing unnoticed

Although the harvest mouse may formerly have been more numerous it must always have been fairly rare since it escaped the notice of naturalists until 1767. Then Gilbert White, the famous clergyman-naturalist of Selborne, discovered it in Hampshire, in southern England. In the same year a distinguished if less well-known naturalist, George Montagu, also discovered it in the neighbouring county of Wiltshire.

Thomas Pennant mentioned 'the less long-tailed field mouse' in his *Zoology*, published in 1768, and finally White described his discovery of it in his *Natural History of Selborne*, published in 1789. In the meantime, however, the Berlin-born naturalist Peter Pallas, who worked for the Russian government and is still famous for many zoological discoveries. had found the mouse on the banks of the Volga and published a scientific description of it in 1771.

class	**Mammalia**
order	**Rodentia**
family	**Muridae**
genus & species	*Micromys minutus* *Old World harvest mouse*
family	**Cricetidae**
genus & species	*Reithrodontomys humulis* *American harvest mouse*

Micromys minutus, the Old World harvest mouse, enjoys a meal. Harvest mice favour seeds—especially crop cereals—but add insects to their menu in the summer months. Although they do not hibernate, they sometimes lay up a store of seeds for the winter. And their wide distribution does not save them from the adverse effect of modern reaping machinery, which not only removes their food and habitat but leaves a far shorter stubble than the old-time scythe.

Hatchet fish

Tiny, strangely-shaped fishes, looking like strips of shiny, crinkled tinfoil—such is the best description of the 15 species of deep-sea hatchet fishes, all of them distant relatives of the salmon. Most of them are 1—2 in. long, the largest being 3½ in. There are 450 of the smaller ones to the lb. Hatchet fishes have high bodies flattened from side to side, resembling the head of a hatchet, the lower surface corresponding with the sharp edge of the hatchet blade. They are covered with large scales which in a few species are missing from the breast and belly, leaving those parts transparent. In all of them the colour of the body is silvery and iridescent. Their eyes are large, their fins are of moderate size and transparent except for the rays supporting them, and along the lower edge of the body and on the underside of the tail are many closely-set light organs. The light from these is usually blue but in some a bright ruby red light has been seen.

The marine hatchet fishes should not be confused with the freshwater fishes given this name (see p 339).

Sensitive telescopic eyes

Marine hatchet fishes live in the twilight zone of the oceans, where only the green and blue rays of light penetrate. They can be found between 300 and 1 500 ft in all tropical and temperate seas. The human eye can detect light at these depths although sensitive photographic plates lowered into the sea register that a very small amount of light penetrates even farther, down to 3 000 ft. Since the human eye can detect a faint light down to 1 500 ft we can suppose the large eye of hatchet fishes, with its large lens, and retina composed of long rods only, is at least as sensitive as the human eye.

How much the light from the hatchet fish's own light organs (which are on the lower edge of the body) help the eyes is problematic. They probably help little, since the eyes are well up on top of the head or directed upwards in some species. In some of these last species the eyes are tubular and are usually described as telescopic. It is even suggested that they may truly be telescopic, magnifying objects seen by the fishes because their focal length, the distance between the lens and the retina, is greater than in the normal eye.

Submarine weightlessness

Hatchet fishes are very light, weighing on average about $\frac{1}{35}$ oz. They have a well-developed swimbladder. These two things together mean they have neutral buoyancy, that is, they neither float up nor sink, but maintain a balance. We are used to the idea of weightlessness in space travel; neutral buoyancy means much the same thing. So hatchet fishes can swim easily and make considerable vertical migrations daily, coming up almost to the surface at night and going down again by day. In these migrations they are following their food, which consists of planktonic animals such as

Aldo Margiocco

copepods and the fry of other fishes. At the same time the hatchet fishes themselves become the prey of carnivorous fishes living near the surface and they are an important part of the food of tunny.

False sea bottoms

Since the end of the Second World War, with the refinement of the echo-sounder, observers on ships of the US Navy in the Pacific noted that their echo-sounder traces showed, in addition to a profile of the sea-bed, a second, sometimes a third or a fourth profile far above the seabed. During the day these 'deep scattering layers', as they came to be called, were at depths of 700—2 400 ft. At nightfall they moved up nearer the surface and became more diffuse. They proved to be made up of the larger animals in the plankton. They need to be about 2½ in. long to reflect back the echoes of the echo-sounder, and the animals giving the traces that make up the deep scattering layers are jellyfishes, large numbers of crustaceans and the larger arrow-worms. In the trace of a deep scattering layer are blobs and marks like an inverted V. These marks were first called tent fish and blob fish, but were later found to be caused by hatchet fishes and lantern fishes. This is an indication of how numerous these two kinds of deep-sea fishes are. When echo-sounders were first being used they often indicated shoals where there should have been deep water. These submerged islands, as they were thought to be, are now known to be deep scattering layers, strata of plankton with the hatchet and lantern fishes feeding under them and forming a temporary and movable ceiling over the vast recesses of the abyssal depths of the oceans.

class	**Pisces**
order	**Salmoniformes**
family	**Sternoptychidae**
genera & species	***Argyropelecus gigas*** ***Sternoptyx diaphana*** *others*

Aldo Margiocco

△ *Dense masses of hatchet fishes help form the phantom sea floor of the deep scattering layer on echo-sounder screens. As in the picture opposite, these are preserved museum specimens.*

▽ *Freshwater hatchet fishes, which do a butterfly-like dance in courtship. Like the marine version, they are named for their shape. These are pygmy hatchet fishes* **Carnegiella marthae***.*

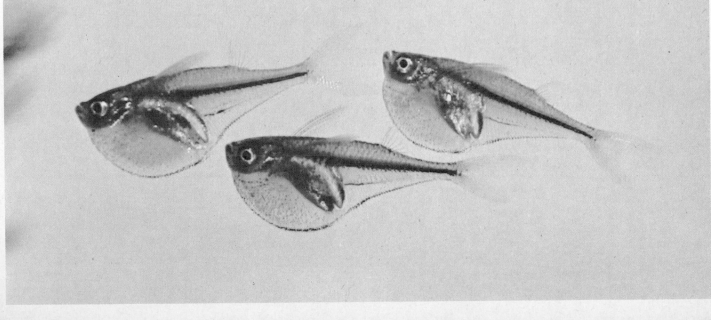

Gene Wolfsheimer

Hawaiian goose

Almost extinct in the wild, the Hawaiian goose has been saved by careful breeding in captivity. It is often known by its Hawaiian name of ne-ne and is a close relative of the Canada goose (p 356) and may well be a descendant of Canada geese that settled in Hawaii thousands of years ago. The Hawaiian goose is a medium-sized goose, weighing 4—5 lb and measuring 23—28 in. long with a fairly long bill. The head and a wide band down the back of the neck are black, the sides of the head and the rest of the neck are tawny with dark stripes running down the neck. The rest of the body is grey-brown with whitish-buff barring, except for a pale brown breast. The female is smaller than the male and has duller plumage.

Danger from lava

The Hawaiian goose was almost wiped out before studies could be made of it in the wild, and the remainder are very secretive and live in very rugged terrain. Hawaiian geese are also called 'lava geese' as they are found among the lava fields near Mauna Loe, a very active volcano. It is quite possible that the wild population could be wiped out by one flow of lava if caught during the flightless period when the geese moult their wing feathers.

It appears that at one time the greater part of the population lived in flocks in the hills and came down to lower ground to breed. In the uplands the Hawaiian goose lived in dry country among the lava and this is no doubt the explanation for the strength of the Hawaiian goose's legs and feet and the small size of the webs between the toes which are half the size of those of other geese.

Back-to-front breeding

Hawaiian geese feed on succulent leaves, stems and flower buds and will strip seeds from grasses. In November the flocks that have been feeding together split up and each pair forms a territory which is defended against other Hawaiian geese. The ganders are extremely bad-tempered and in captivity pairs have to be isolated from one another. Not only are the territory and the brood defended vigorously against all comers, the ganders sometimes attack their own mates.

The nest is a hollow in the ground where 3—5 eggs are laid, generally on alternate days, and incubated by the goose while the gander stands guard. The goslings are brown with whitish markings. They run about on large feet under the protection of their parents, feeding on plants like watercress and sowthistle. Their feathers do not appear for 5 weeks and the young geese cannot fly until they are 3 months old. Canada geese can fly at half this age, but they can grow much more rapidly because the days are longer in northern latitudes, so there is more time for feeding. The Hawaiian geese also breed from November to January—the time of year when the days are shortest. This is a most unusual time to breed and no reason is known for it. The goose starts to breed when 2 years old, and lays 2—3 clutches a year.

Wrong close season

Because no one studied the habits of Hawaiian geese, it was not known for a long

A triumph for conservation: these ne-ne are the descendants of three sent to Britain in 1950.

time that they bred in the 'wrong' half of the year. As a result the open season for shooting them was fixed during their breeding season. This was, however, only one of several reasons for their decline. They were never abundant and the total population when Europeans arrived in Hawaii was probably about 25 000. Dogs, pigs, rats and cats went wild and preyed on the geese, but their decline became marked when mongooses were liberated on the island.

Saving the ne-ne

From an estimated 25 000 the population of the Hawaiian goose had sunk to 34 by 1950. Some 17 were in captivity, and 17 were still alive in their natural home. Efforts were then made to preserve the species. The wild ones were protected and stocks of captive ones were increased by breeding, notably at the Severn Wildfowl Trust at Slimbridge, England. In captivity it was found that the geese were liable to desert their eggs, which had to be hatched under bantams, and some goslings had to be helped out of their shells. The hatching rate is considerably lower than that of other geese in the Slimbridge collection; this may

be another reason for the small size of the original population and the ease with which the numbers have been reduced.

By 1957 the numbers had risen to 129; at least 35 were wild and 49 of the captives were living outside Hawaii. Of these 40 were at Slimbridge. The Slimbridge flock grew apace and in 1962 there were enough to fly 32 back to the Pacific and release them on Maui, with more in the next 2 years. In 1964 the world population of Hawaiian geese was between 380 and 420, of which 250–300 were wild or captive on Hawaii and Maui. By 1969 the population had risen to over 800, more than half of which were living wild.

The Hawaiian goose is lucky as the keeping of wildfowl is a popular pursuit throughout the world. Its plight came to the notice of people who were keen on saving it and were already in a position to keep a small stock and breed them.

Unfortunately more and more animals are going to find themselves in the same danger as the Hawaiian goose and even if they are saved from extinction they will never really be wild animals. Some, like Père David's deer, are already confined to parks and zoos and as the human popula-

tion expands many animals will be able to survive only under protection. Numbers will either have to be conserved carefully, by providing breeding sites and removing enemies, or even kept down to prevent overcrowding in their semi-artificial homes, as elephants have to be reduced in number in African game parks. This sort of conservation takes time, money and space, and it may be necessary to decide which animals should be preserved. The Hawaiian goose and Père David's deer are flourishing in their new homes. The whooping crane (p 562) with its long migration, is very vulnerable; it is sometimes suggested that its conservation is doomed and that money spent on it could be used for saving animals with a better chance of survival.

class	**Aves**
order	**Anseriformes**
family	**Anatidae**
genus & species	***Branta sandvicensis***

Ne-ne or Hawaiian geese flaunt a dark brown collar and a distinctive barred plumage.

F Vollmar: WWF

△ *Poplar hawk laying eggs. The following sequence shows the development of another prominent hawk—Acherontia atropos, the death's-head.*

△ *The last moments of egghood; inside the shell the head and jaws of the infant caterpillar can be clearly seen as it prepares to break out.*

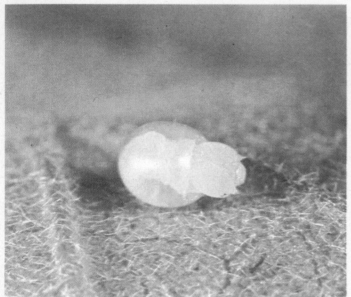

△ *Take it slowly: out comes the head followed by the front segments.*
▽ *A last look at the old home? Not at all—this is its first meal!*

△ *Progress quickens with the front legs out and getting a good grip.*
▽ *Leave no litter: a methodical nibble round the edge of the shell.*

Through the last barrier: out comes the adult moth after the completion of pupation.

Hawk moth heavyweight, the death's-head hawk gets its name from the eerie 'skull' pattern on the back of its thorax. These buccaneer moths plunder beehives of their honey.

Hawk moth

Hawk moths—also called sphinx moths— make up the family Sphingidae, large, thick-bodied moths found throughout the world. Most of the 900 species are tropical and only 23 are known in Europe. Of these, 18 have been recorded from Britain, the remaining five being southern species.

Hawk moths have a thick, torpedo-shaped body, long narrow forewings, small hindwings and large eyes. The tongue or proboscis is well developed and sometimes remarkably long. The larvae are stout and usually have a spike or horn at the hind end of the back. Many of them when molested rear up in a characteristic way which reminded early entomologists of the Sphinx of Egypt, which explains the name of the family.

Swiftest of insects?

The hawk moths all have powerful, well controlled flight and most of them can hover like hummingbirds when feeding from flowers. The little hummingbird hawk looks remarkably like a tiny bird as it hovers in front of flowers; honeysuckle, jasmine and valerian are particularly attractive to it. Some of the larger species are probably the swiftest fliers of all insects, but since almost all of them fly by night their speeds are extremely hard to measure. The fastest speeds so far measured for insects are for dragonflies. Speeds of 45, even 55 mph have been reported for some dragonflies, but hawk moths have even thicker and more muscular bodies and their wings and flight muscles are more efficiently designed than those of dragonflies. So although only 33 mph has been recorded for a hawk moth the chances are that they achieve greater speeds than this. A few smaller hawk moths fly by day at high speeds but their speeds have not yet been measured.

A hawk moth found at rest usually cannot fly immediately because its body temperature is too low. If one of them is disturbed when at rest it will rapidly vibrate its wings for a minute or more, and then take to the air. This raises its internal temperature to the point at which it can fly. A hawk moth almost literally warms up its engine before taking off.

As might be expected, the hawk moth's powerful flight is associated with migratory habits. The convolvulus hawk is a huge grey moth with a very wide range, from Africa and Europe across Asia to Australia. It breeds in Africa and regularly flies northwards, crossing the Alps with ease and appearing in Britain in late summer and autumn; it has even been recorded from Iceland. The equally large and more heavily built death's-head hawk is seen far less frequently in Britain, but occasionally flies from North Africa in swarms.

Putting a bold face on it: tropical hawk caterpillars have disconcerting 'eye' patterns.

One of the most striking and attractive hawk moth caterpillars is that of the privet hawk Sphinx ligustri, looking like a cross between a pantomime horse and a heraldic monster.

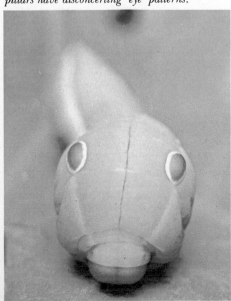

The outsize proboscis of the convolvulus hawk.

Convolvulus hawk feeding from the nectar of night-flowering sweet tobacco.

Feeds on potato poisons

Hawk moth caterpillars feed on the leaves of plants and trees and the various species usually confine their attention to a fairly narrow range of plants related to each other. Both their Latin and English names often indicate the food plant, as in poplar hawk moth, lime hawk moth and privet hawk moth. The huge caterpillar of the death's-head hawk, 5 in. long, feeds on plants of the family Solanaceae, most of which are poisonous to us and other animals. Potatoes are one of these and at one time the caterpillars were common in potato fields, but spraying against blight has made them very rare. If you do find a death's-head caterpillar, remember that the pupa requires warmth if it is to produce a moth. The pupae cannot survive in the open in Britain, so even when the caterpillars were more common they lived in vain, never completing their life history.

The caterpillars of many hawk moths are big enough to look rather like snakes. Some tropical species have false eyes and other markings on the front part of the body and these, with appropriate movements and postures, give the caterpillar a vividly snake-like appearance which is probably effective in scaring off hungry birds, as are the conspicuous 'eyes' on the fore part of the elephant hawk moth caterpillar.

Most of the hawk moth caterpillars pupate underground in an earthen cell, but a few, including the two elephant hawks, spin an open-mesh cocoon among debris or under herbage on the surface of the ground. In those species in which the proboscis is greatly developed it is contained during the pupal stage in a curved or coiled sheath at the front of the pupa. This is present in the pupa of the privet hawk and is very conspicuous in that of the convolvulus hawk.

Adults suck nectar

Almost all of the adult moths feed on nectar, hovering and probing the flowers with the long tubular proboscis, which is coiled like a watch-spring when not in use. That of the convolvulus hawk is extraordinary: when fully extended it is about 4 in. long, and can take nectar from flowers, such as those of tobacco plants, with very long corolla tubes.

This species has, however, by no means the longest tongue of all hawk moths. In 1891 the English naturalist AR Wallace noticed that there was an orchid native to Madagascar, with its nectaries situated at a depth of 10—13 in. No insect was known that could reach them and so act as a pollinator, and Wallace predicted that a hawk moth would be found that could do this. In 1903 just such a moth was discovered in Madagascar with a proboscis 11 in. long. It was named *Macrosilia morgani* and received the appropriate subspecific name *predicta*.

The death's-head hawk has a short, stiff proboscis, quite unsuitable for delicately probing flowers, and it robs bees' nests and hives of their honey. Most modern hives are designed to prevent its entry, but the bee-

Head-on view of the large elephant hawk Deilephila elpenor.

Elephant hawk after emergence from pupa.

*Narrow-bordered bee hawk **Hemaris tityus**.*

*Handsome Australian—**Hippotion scrofa**.*

Living up to its name: lime hawk on lime leaves.

keepers of a century and more ago knew it well, and the early entomologists called it the 'bee tyger'. Its modern name is based on a rather fanciful resemblance in the markings on its thorax to a human skull. Another curious feature of it is the ability to squeak quite loudly, both as a caterpillar and as a moth. The caterpillar stridulates, but the adult moth squeaks by forcing air out through an opening at the base of the proboscis. Beekeepers long ago suggested the squeaks quieted the bees, who took it to be their queen squeaking, so making it easier for the moth to take their honey. In recent years we have been able, using very small microphones, to listen to the queen bee squeaking.

Fake eye trick

When mounted in a collection the eyed hawk seems one of the most beautiful of British hawk moths. The elegantly shaped forewings are marbled in shades of violet-grey and on each of the pink and ochreous hindwings is a sharply drawn blue-and-black 'eye'. However, an eyed hawk moth sitting at rest, with the hindwings covered, looks very like a chance arrangement of curled-up dead leaves. If discovered by the sharp eyes of a searching bird and pecked, it immediately reacts by lifting the forewings and revealing what appears to the enemy to be a pair of lurid, staring eyes of a size to suggest a cat or an owl. Experiments have been carried out in which a bird was persuaded to attack an eyed hawk, and the bird always started back in alarm. Some bolder birds overcame their fears and returned to the attack, but some were wholly daunted and left the moth alone, so we can take it that the lives of some eyed hawk moths are saved by this device. If the hindwings are rubbed and the pattern obliterated the moth will go through the same performance as usual, but the birds will always kill and eat it. The two bee hawks, with partly scaleless and transparent wings, look very much like bumblebees and so may gain some protection.

phylum	**Arthropoda**
class	**Insecta**
order	**Lepidoptera**
family	**Sphingidae**
genera & species	***Acherontia atropos*** *death's-head hawk* ***Deilephila elpenor*** *elephant hawk* ***Hemaris fuciformis*** *broad-bordered bee hawk* ***H. tityus*** *narrow-bordered bee hawk* ***Herse convolvuli*** *convolvulus hawk* ***Laothoe populi*** *poplar hawk* ***Macroglossum stellatarum*** *hummingbird hawk* ***Mimas tiliae*** *lime hawk* ***Sphinx ligustri*** *privet hawk* *others*

Like the aptly-named hummingbird hawk moth, the elephant hawk looks amazingly like a small bird as it hovers in front of a flower to feed.

Submarine reptile with an armour-plated upper deck: a hawksbill shoulders its way through the crowds at Marineland, Florida.

Hawksbill

The hawksbill turtle is the source of 'tortoiseshell' once widely used for combs and spectacle frames as well as for ornamental items such as fans and cigarette boxes. The introduction of plastics at first destroyed the market for tortoise-shell, but no plastic has ever rivalled tortoiseshell for its translucent colouring and the natural material is being used again, especially in curios.

One of the smallest turtles, although larger than the Ridley turtle, the hawksbill usually has a shell around 2 ft long and weighs about 100 lb. The record hawksbill weighs 280 lb. The shell is largely brown on top, often with dark blotches at the front. The plastron, the underpart of the shell, is yellow. The name hawksbill is derived from the hooked 'beak' which is far more prominent than the snouts of other turtles.

Hawksbills are found in tropical seas around the world. On the Pacific side of America they are found as far north as Mexico, and as far south as Peru. On
the Atlantic side the warm Gulf Stream allows them to spread farther north. They have been found breeding in Florida and occasionally they stray as far north as Massachusetts, and even to the Orkney Islands on the eastern side of the Atlantic. To the south hawksbills reach southern Brazil, and although rare or even non-existent on the west coast of Africa they turn up again around Madagascar, and in other parts of the Indian Ocean.

Home-loving turtles

Unlike green or Ridley turtles, hawksbills are found only in scattered numbers on their quiet breeding and feeding grounds. Every secluded beach is visited by a few female hawksbills in search of egg-laying sites and some hawksbills are almost certain to be found feeding around any coral reef or coral rock. Hawksbills do not migrate regularly like green turtles (p 948) but appear to stay more or less in one place, although some do wander long distances. They are slow swimmers compared with green turtles and often have large barnacles on their shells, whereas the green turtles are found bearing only small barnacles.

The hawksbill has never been as important a source of food as the green turtle, so its habits have not been so well studied. A hawksbill did, however, provide the first record of a turtle returning to the same place to breed. In 1794 a Dutch officer attached a ring to the flipper of a hawksbill which, by a surprising trick of fate, was found 30 years later on the same beach.

Poisoned flesh

Although they eat water plants, hawksbills prefer animal food such as crabs, fish and planktonic animals, cracking open crabs and shellfish with their powerful 'beaks'. This results in their flesh being less acceptable to humans as it is often very fishy. Hawksbill flesh is usually eaten by only the poorest people. It may also sometimes be poisonous and there is a record of 24 people being taken ill after eating a hawksbill; seven of them died. In some places fishermen test for poison by first throwing the hawksbill's liver to the crows. If they reject the liver, then the hawksbill is poisonous. The poisonous quality might be due to the hawksbills' habit of eating jellyfish and Portuguese men-o'-war. It attacks them with its eyes closed, but they no doubt get stung by the nematocysts (see anemone, p 44) in the mouth and throat as they swallow the jellyfish. It is probable that, like other animals that feed on poisonous creatures, hawksbills are themselves totally or partially immune to their prey's poison.

Long breeding season

As well as breeding at well-spaced-out intervals, hawksbills also lay their eggs at almost any time of the year. Peak laying takes place in May and June in the Caribbean and September to November in the Indian Ocean. In both areas the green turtle breeds a few months later. As they share breeding beaches a staggered laying time is an advantage.

A hawskbill lays probably every 2—3 years. Each clutch contains, on average, 160 round eggs, 1½ in. diameter. As a female crawls up the beach—flippers working alternately instead of together like the green turtle—she nuzzles the sand at intervals, apparently searching for a suitable site for the nest. It is not known what conditions are necessary for the nest; it may be connected with the dampness or even the coarseness of the sand. She does not dig a body pit like the green turtle but only an egg hole about 10 in. deep. The eggs hatch in 50 days and the young turtles have the same hazardous dash to the sea as baby green turtles.

Tortoiseshell plates

Tortoiseshell has been used for hundreds of years; since early times the Chinese and Japanese used it in works of art and the Romans used it as a veneer for furniture. Tortoiseshell was popular because of its translucent or clear amber colouring flecked with black, red, green or white. Also known as 'carey', it is obtained by soaking the hawksbill's body in boiling water, which loosens the plates from the carapace. They can then be moulded to shape by being softened in hot water, or several plates could be fused together by pressing them in a steam chamber. The result was not only a raw material that would take on a beautiful polish but an extremely good, if expensive, 'plastic' that could be worked into many different shapes.

The advent of synthetic plastics appeared to have saved the hawksbill from possible extinction and 30 or so years ago tortoiseshell had no commercial value. Then the demand rose again, as no plastic could rival real tortoiseshell for beauty and curios and souvenirs of tortoiseshell became popular as the post-war boom in tourism developed. In 1967 a hawksbill turtle could fetch 14 dollars, more than a week's wages in some parts of the world. Up to 12 lb of tortoiseshell can be obtained from one turtle and, in addition, its skin makes a very high-class leather.

Alice Brown

△ *Out of its element: a barnacle encrusted old salt lumbers ashore, leaving a trail like a tank.*

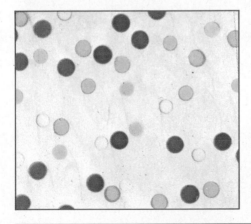

In the sensitive 'back plate' (retina) of a turtle's eye are thousands of oil droplets, some coloured, others transparent, shown on the microscope slide at left with no staining at all. These tiny spheres are contained in the cone-shaped cells of the retina, the ones which are usually sensitive to colour in other animals. A diagram of one of these cones containing an oil droplet is shown below. Light enters from the left, passes through the nucleus (the grey globe), on through the yellow oil, and into light-sensitive pigment (dark area, extreme right). It is possible, but by no means proved, that the droplets act as a colour filter, enabling the turtle to have colour vision.

class	**Reptilia**
order	**Chelonia**
family	**Chelonidae**
genus & species	*Eretmochelys imbricata*

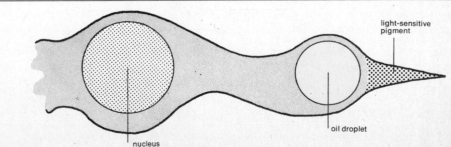

Hedgehog

*Except for garden birds there is probably
no wild animal so regularly fed and so
popularly 'adopted' as the hedgehog,
hedgepig, or urchin, an animal remarkable
for its coat of spines and its habit of rolling
defensively into a ball.*

*The male, or boar, grows to 10¼ in. long,
with an inch of tail, the sow being on
average ¾ in. shorter. The weight is up
to 2⅔ lb. A hedgehog's neck and body
are short in relation to its bulk. The
back and top of the head are coated
with sharply-pointed spines, ¾ in. long,
with each spine set at an angle to the skin.
The rest of the body is clothed in coarse
hair. All four feet have five clawed toes
and five pads on the sole.*

*Besides the European hedgehog (so
called although it ranges across Asia as
well) there are 14 other species in southwest Europe, Asia and Africa. All are
alike in habits and differ in appearance in
small details only.*

Twilight forager

The hedgehog lives in a variety of habitats,
wherever there is vegetation cover or
enough dry leaf litter into which it can retire
to sleep through the day. A hedge bottom is
a typical place to find the animal asleep. At
twilight it comes out to forage. When undisturbed it moves quickly over the ground,
despite its short legs, but any unfamiliar
sound or movement makes it stop dead and
draw the spines on the top of the head forward. This is preparatory to rolling up if its
alarm increases, the head and legs being
withdrawn and the edges of the prickly
mantle drawn around them to present an
almost complete ball of spines. A hedgehog
climbs and swims well, but usually keeps to
the ground. Its sight seems to be poor but
its sense of smell and hearing are acute.

Wide choice of diet

Snails, slugs, insects and worms form the
normal hedgehog diet. Mice, rats, frogs,
lizards and snakes may be eaten at times. It
has sometimes been said that hedgehogs eat
no plant material, but they have been seen to
eat acorns and berries and tame hedgehogs
have been known to eat either apple, pear,
orange or some other fruit. An individual
will usually take one or other of these fruits.
Hedgehogs have often been condemned for
taking hens' eggs and several people have
tested tame or captive animals and found
that they show no interest in eggs placed
deliberately within their reach or else they
are unable to open the egg even if they
show interest. Possibly a hedgehog that has
found a cracked or broken egg may develop
a taste for them. Certainly it is now proven
beyond doubt that some hedgehogs take
the eggs of wild birds, including partridges
and pheasants.

Rubbery-spined babies

The breeding season is between May and
July but there may be a second litter during
August and September. After a gestation

△ *Innocents abroad: unable to curl and gain
even the scant protection of their few early
prickles, a pair of vulnerable young hedgehogs
blunder through leaf litter around their home.*

▷ *Not for much longer: a female hedgehog
suckles her nearly-weaned young. Babies grow
their adult spines, wean and start active
wandering at about 1 month old.*

▽ *Morning parade: a mother inspects her
prickly platoon of very young recruits.*

△ *Panic action: ignoring her offspring, a very frightened hedgehog curls into a defensive ball.*

▽ *The face of suspicion: spines at the ready, a disgruntled hedgehog tries to assess the potential danger of the photographer.*

period of 31—40 days a litter of 3—7 blind, deaf and helpless young are born, each $2\frac{1}{4}$— $3\frac{1}{4}$ in. long and weighing $\frac{1}{3}$—$\frac{2}{3}$ oz, and sparsely clad with pale flexible spines. Between 36—60 hours after birth a second coat of darker spines appears between the first spines but the young hedgehog is unable to roll up until 11 days old and 3 days later its eyes open, first one and then the other, over a period of 3 days. At this time a third set of spines begins to grow through, each spine ringed with a dark band in the middle and a light band either side. The first two sets of spines are then shed when the baby is a month old and has started to make short journeys from the nest and is being weaned. Its weight doubles in 7 days from birth and is increased tenfold by the age of 7 weeks, but sexual maturity is not reached until the following year. The mother alone looks after the youngsters, the father taking no part at all.

Intermittent winter sleep

Hibernation covers the period from October to late March or April. Some individuals sleep through the whole period, but in others sleep is intermittent until December or even later, so it is not unusual to see a hedgehog out and about on frosty nights, or even in snow, until the end of the year. It seems likely that sleep, from October to December, is less profound in younger hedgehogs. For hibernating, hedgehogs choose a hole in a bank, perhaps one that has been enlarged by a colony of wasps, but more commonly it is the cavity between the buttress roots of a well-grown tree or under a heap of leaf or brush litter, a favourite place being a compost heap. This is lined with dry leaves and moss, carried in the mouth, and the process appears to be started towards the end of summer. During hibernation the body is nourished by fat accumulated during the summer but the energy requirements are low, for the temperature of the body drops, breathing is so slight that it can hardly be detected and the pulse-rate drops considerably. Within the body is a dark brown gland which has been named the hibernating gland. It is now spoken of as brown fat, comparable to that found in a similar position (mainly around the neck and shoulders) in many baby mammals, and in some adults, such as bats and rats.

Investigations carried out in 1963 showed the brown fat to be a kind of electric blanket. Its cells are larger and contain more fat droplets than normal white fat cells and they release heat 20 times faster. In addition their heat production increases rapidly as the temperature of the surrounding air drops, so this dark-coloured fat acts like a thermostatically controlled electric blanket.

Despite the profound sleep of hibernation the hedgehog is still in touch with its surroundings to some extent. It will, for example, respond to sharp clicks by raising its spines slightly at each click. Should the temperature drop too much, the heart, which remains warmer than the tissues on the outside of the body, automatically begins to beat faster. The animal resumes its temperature control, becomes once more warm-blooded and will resume normal activity for a while, afterwards falling asleep again to continue its hibernation.

Jane Burton: Photo Res

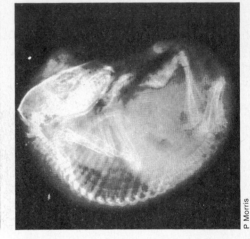

◁ *Unexplained behaviour: a hedgehog 'self-anointing', throwing head over shoulder to put foaming saliva onto its back spines.*
◁▽ *A folk-tale illustrated: hedgehogs rolling on apples to carry them away on their spines. (From a 12c manuscript in the British Museum.)*
▽ *Worm's eye view: hedgehog rolling up, exposing a ball of rigid spines to a predator above and the minimum surface area if rolled over.*
▽▽ *X-ray of rolled-up hedgehog shows how complete the action is; head almost touches tail.*

Self-anointing

A strange and, until recent years, little-known habit of hedgehogs is that of self-anointing. The animal, meeting a substance for the first time, will lick it repeatedly while its mouth becomes filled with a frothy saliva. The substance inducing this may be a cigar end, a handkerchief, shoe polish, the skin of a dead toad, a piece of wood and so on. Whatever the substance, when the mouth is full of foam, the hedgehog raises itself on its front legs and throws the head first to one side then to the other, placing flecks of foam on the spines with its tongue. There is, as yet, no satisfactory explanation for this remarkable behaviour.

Tough fighters

Foxes and badgers are the principal enemies apart from man. Rats sometimes kill them but in a straight fight a hedgehog and a rat are fairly evenly matched. A hedgehog is a match for an adder also, being immune to its poison. Hedgehogs are immune to all but a few poisons and even for these abnormally large doses are needed to kill them. Gamekeepers often persecute hedgehogs to prevent them taking eggs of ground nesting game birds. They generally do this with baited cage traps or drop pits.

Thieving milk

Two of the most persistent legends are that hedgehogs will impale fruit such as apples, pears and strawberries on their spines and carry it away. There have been representations in pottery, in illuminated manuscripts as well as in the written record for at least 2 000 years yet very few scientists are prepared to give credence to this in spite of at least two photographs taken of it happening.

Another equally persistent belief which also arouses scientific scepticism is that hedgehogs will suck the milk from cows. For centuries hedgehogs have had a bounty on their heads and the churchwardens' accounts in England record the sums of money paid out annually for the slaughter of hedgehogs because they take milk from cows. The usual explanation is that this belief arises because from time to time somebody sees a hedgehog searching for insects under the udder of a cow lying on the ground. It is then argued that if the cow has a leaky teat the hedgehog, with its known fondness for milk, will be bound to lick the oozing milk and so give the impression of deliberately extracting it. An experiment carried out in 1968 using an artificial teat for feeding calves showed that a wild hedge-

hog deliberately seized the teat in its mouth, tugged at it with the same action that a cow-man would use in milking the cow and so drank all the milk in the feeding teat. The hedgehog repeated this every time the teat was refilled, doing so without hesitation and always in the characteristic manner. In the *Veterinary Review* for May and June 1967 are two reports by a vet of injury to cows' teats, and these are supported by photographs. It seems clear that veterinary surgeons have known for a long time that hedgehogs will not only take milk from cows deliberately but will lacerate the teats in doing so. It is of interest to note that the members of the community most disposed to accept the story of hedgehogs milking cows have been the farmers and their cowmen. One reason why they are so emphatic is that cows' teats are injured only during the spring and summer and not during the winter—when hedgehogs are hibernating.

class	**Mammalia**
order	**Insectivora**
family	**Erinaceidae**
genus & species	*Erinaceus europaeus*

Heliozoan

The Heliozoa or 'sun-animalcules' are single celled animals, or Protista, mostly living in freshwater. More or less spherical, the largest $\frac{1}{25}$ in. diameter, they are named for the ray-like pseudopodia projecting in all directions from their surface. These pseudopodia differ from those of amoeba in being long and narrow, and each is supported by a stiff central filament (axopodium) rising from deep in the body. The rest of the cell, forming the body of the sun-animalcule, consists of a central mass of endoplasm containing a nucleus, or, in some species, many nuclei, perhaps 20 – 500 of them.

Surrounding the endoplasm is a layer of ectoplasm often enclosed in a jelly- or mucus-like envelope. Both layers have a foamy appearance. Some heliozoans have a skeleton in the outer layer made up of foreign bodies, such as sand grains or the shells of diatoms, or of spicules of silica laid down by the animal itself. The spicules are often arranged without particular pattern, but they may project from the surface among the axopodia as in Acanthocystis, for example. Most heliozoans are free-living, but some are anchored by a stalk, like the marine Wagnerella. This consists of the usual spherical body with axopodia radiating from its surface but connected to an attached base by a stalk $\frac{1}{25}$in. long surrounded by silica spicules and a slimy material. The 'head' can be withdrawn into the tube so formed.

Microfauna of still waters

Among wellknown heliozoans are *Actinosphaerium eichhornia*, and *Actinophrys sol*, about $\frac{1}{250}$ in. across. These live on plants in still freshwater and pull themselves around by slightly contracting the fibre-like axopodia. These minute filaments are surprisingly adaptable, in so primitive an animal. Although normally held rigid, they can be bent and there is a flow of protoplasm in both directions along them. One species is reported to be able to swim by rapid beats of the axopodia.

Freshwater animals usually absorb water by osmosis (see amoeba, p 34). Heliozoans, like amoeba, have contractile vacuoles and these are used to pump out excess water in the ectoplasm then collapse as their contents are discharged to the exterior. Marine heliozoans have no contractile vacuoles.

Co-operative feeding

Heliozoans feed on other protistans, small single celled algae and small rotifers and crustaceans. When one of these becomes stuck to an axopodium the latter suddenly shortens, sometimes impaling the prey on other axopodia. Alternatively, the axopodium may bend around the prey and so force it towards the heliozoan's surface. Some scientists have reported seeing the prey become still, as if paralysed, when it touched an axopodium. As the prey is drawn towards the animal's surface, it becomes enveloped in a cup of ectoplasm which may grow out and around it to enclose it. Digestion takes place within the endoplasm and indigestible matter is passed out through the surface at the nearest point. Just as there is no permanent opening to take in food, so there is none to void waste. In some species, several individuals may combine to digest a large food object, perhaps a small crustacean, and when they do this their bodies become fused together until digestion is completed. Then they part company. Some kinds of sun-animalcules, like *Actinophrys*, seem to supplement their diet by making indirect use of the sun's rays. They contain very small single celled algae within their ectoplasm known as zoochlorellae which synthesize food in sunlight.

Complicated reproduction

Reproduction is usually by splitting in two, a process known as binary fission, or else by budding. In some heliozoans the division is incomplete so the new cells remain united, thus forming colonies. Sexual reproduction can also occur. As the food supply begins to fail in autumn the sexual phase of *Actinosphaerium* is preceded by a reduction in the number of nuclei, most of which break up. The animal becomes rounded and secretes a thick gelatinous cyst around itself, and the whole becomes stuck to some hard object. Each remaining nucleus becomes enclosed by a small amount of cytoplasm. The nucleus plus this cytoplasm divides in two; each half divides twice more with a halving

in the number of chromosomes (meiosis). All the division products of each of the two cells except one degenerate, while the remaining pair unite, again just as in the fertilisation of an egg by a sperm, though here the cells are alike.

Jekyll and Hyde

A group often classed with the heliozoans is known as the helioflagellates, though whether they should be is a matter of debate. They present a problem for the tidy-minded biologist who would place each species in a neat category, for an individual helioflagellate may look like a heliozoan one moment, then, in a few seconds, lose its axopodia, change its shape and swim off with a pair of flagella—an undoubted flagellate. At other times the animal may look halfway between a heliozoan and a flagellate. A Gruber who, in 1882, first described such an animal called it *Dimorpha mutans*—the changing two-shaped one.

The change from one to the other is brought about by changes in the salt content of the water. Thus specimens of *Dimorpha floridanis* in lake water were true heliozoans but, under the microscope, changed to flagellates in 5–30 seconds when distilled water was added. In the most dilute solutions the body of the flagellate is rounded, but in more concentrated solutions the body is drawn out and pointed at the hind end. The reverse can be brought about by increasing the amount of salt in the water as, for instance, by letting some of the water evaporate. It can also be brought about if the water is slightly disturbed, as when a larger protistan or a rotifer swims by. The reappearance of the axopodia may take several minutes, but it can be all over in less than a second and so rapid that the nucleus becomes impaled on one of the axopodia.

phylum	**Protista**
class	**Sarcodina**
order	**Heliozoa**
genera	***Acanthocystis, Actinophrys Actinosphaerium Dimorpha, Wagnerella***

Left: A pair of 'sun-cells'. Right: Heliozoan ***Actinosphaerium arachnoideum,*** *× 750 size.*

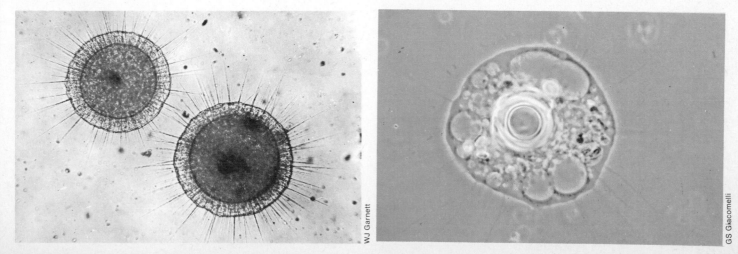

WJ Garnett

GS Giacomelli

Barry Driscoll

The hellbender: 2 ft of supple sliminess, with a bite like an angry rat-trap—small wonder that some people think it is poisonous.

Hellbender

This is a giant salamander of North America, one of two species, with a third living in China and Japan. The origin of the name is not known, although it may be connected with its grotesque, almost sinister appearance and pliable body.

The hellbender can be up to 30 in. long, from light to dark brown to nearly black with scattered blackish spots. Its body and head are flattened, the head broad with a wide mouth and small eyes. The tail is stout at the base, flattened and oar-like at the end, accounting for ⅓ of the animal's total length. The skin is slimy and thrown into irregular folds along the flanks. The legs are moderately well developed, with four toes on the front feet and five on each hindfoot.

Its range is from the Great Lakes through the eastern United States to Georgia and Louisiana.

The Chinese giant salamander can be up to 41½ in. long, and is much heavier than the hellbender, with bead-like 'barbels' on the chin. The Japanese giant salamander is up to 5 ft long, with a weight of up to 90 lb.

Different ways of breathing

Hellbenders live in rivers and large streams with a rapid flow of water and, usually, a rocky bed. They swim by wriggling the body, waggling the head from side to side (unusual for a swimming animal) and lie up under large stones or among rocks by day, coming out at night to feed. They breathe by internal gills, with two gill openings on either side of the neck. These are in addition to lungs. When living in the still water of an aquarium a hellbender must rise to the surface every 25—40 minutes to take air. In well-aerated running water, it surfaces less often. Breathing is also carried out

through the skin, the folds of which are richly supplied with surface blood vessels.

Probably because of its ugliness, and also its ability to bite hard when handled, the hellbender has the reputation of being poisonous, which is completely untrue.

Catholic tastes

Hellbenders eat almost any animal small enough to be swallowed, including worms, water snails, insect larvae, crayfish, as well as frogs and fishes, all captured with a quick sideways snatch. They do not feed when the temperature of the water is under 10°C/ 50°F. Otherwise they feed well, taking dead animal flesh as well as live animals.

Males eat the eggs

In August the male begins to remove silt from the downstream side of a rock, creating a bowl in which the female will later lay her eggs. These are 3/16 in. diameter and are laid in a long jelly string which she contrives to press in under the rock. The jelly around each egg swells to the size of a grape. Each jelly garland contains around 300—450 eggs. They are fertilised as they are being laid, and after this the male takes over their care. In fact, he eats a number of them, as well as many of the larvae.

The larvae are a little over 1 in. long when they finally burst out of the jelly envelope, 2 or more months later. Each larva has external gills. Its hindlegs are at first paddle-shaped with no sign of toes, the front legs show signs of two toes. The larva swims with its flattened rudder-like tail and, once the remains of the egg yolk are used, it alternately swims against the current and probes the mud at the bottom of the river with its snout, searching for worms and other small aquatic animals. The external gills are absorbed when the larva is 4—5 in. long and 1—1½ years old.

Hellbenders do not mature until at least 5 years old, and they have a long lifespan, 30 years at least. One Japanese giant salamander lived 52 years in captivity.

Turtle enemies

The enemies of these graceless amphibians are mainly freshwater turtles and carnivorous fishes. The Japanese giant salamander is fished with a line and hook and used for food.

Swamps and giants

The distribution of the giant salamanders, two in northern Asia and one in North America, geographically separated, reminds us of the distribution of the lungfishes in the southern hemisphere, which are found in eastern Australia, central Africa and South America. This is a familiar pattern for groups of animals that are of ancient lineage and are now dying out. Their final demise may be a long way off but the decline is well under way. In appearance, at least, the giant salamanders resemble our reconstructions of the earliest known amphibians. These were salamander-like, 7 ft long and lived 300 million years ago in the swamps which have given us our coal measures. Another famous giant salamander lived in Europe about 12 million years ago. It was 3½ ft long and a close relative of the three surviving giant salamanders. Its name is *Andrias scheuchzeri* and its fossil skeleton was described in 1731 by a Swiss physician, Johann Jacob Scheuchzer. He thought it was the skeleton of a sinner overwhelmed in the Deluge and named it *Homo diluvii testis*—man, a witness of the deluge.

class	**Amphibia**
order	**Caudata**
family	**Cryptobranchidae**
genera & species	***Cryptobranchus alleganiensis*** hellbender ***Megalobatrachus davidianus*** Chinese giant salamander ***M. japonicus*** Japanese giant salamander

Hermit crab

Hermit crabs live in abandoned sea snail shells, and in all of them the form of the body is modified accordingly. The banana-shaped abdomen, protected in its 'hermitage', is soft and curves to the right to fit the inside of the snail shell. The front end of the body has the hard covering typical of crabs and lobsters and the right claw, larger than the left, is used to close the entrance of the shell. The two pairs of legs behind the claw are used in walking, but the next two pairs are small and are used to grip the shell. The last pair of limbs on the abdomen, which in a lobster form part of the tail fan, are sickle-shaped and used for holding onto the central column of the shell. There are swimmerets on the left side of the abdomen only.

The robber or coconut crab **Birgus latro** of the South Sea Islands, is a land-living hermit crab several pounds in weight and 6 in. across. The adult has lost the shell-dwelling habit and although the abdomen is still twisted it has a hard covering and is kept tucked under the thorax. The stone crabs **Lithodes,** found off the coasts of Britain, although looking like true crabs, show their hermit crab ancestry in their small asymmetrical abdomen.

Pre-fab houses
The common hermit crab of European seas is the soldier crab *Pagurus bernhardus*. Normally only the young are found on the shore, their red and yellow front ends projecting from winkle, topshell or dog whelk shells. They are nimble despite their burdens and are well-protected from the pounding of waves and from drying up when the tide is out. The older ones reach a length of 5 in., live in deeper water and occupy the larger shells of common and hard whelks. On tropical coasts live semi-terrestrial hermit crabs of the genus *Coenobita*. These usually occupy ordinary snail shells, but East Indian coenobites have been seen wearing such odd

*The face of a squatter: hermit crab **Pagurus megistos.** The massive right claw acts as a 'door' when the crab retreats into its shell. The legs are adapted to the crab's home-changing habits. Only the two pairs behind the claws are used for walking; the rest grip the shell.*

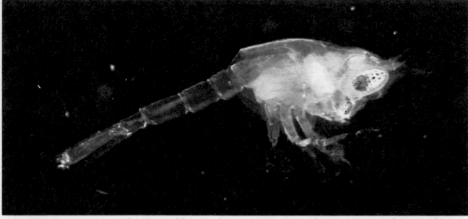

△ *Drifting youth: one of the shrimp-like zoea larvae of* **Pagurus alatus**. *After moulting its skin four times as it grows, the larva finds a home. It will reach maturity after a year, perhaps more.*

△ *Vulnerable househunter:* **Paguristes oculatus** *in its birthday suit. Without a shell, the crab becomes a choice morsel for predatory fish, so hermits usually shed shells with a new one nearby.*

△ *Cutaway shell shows how the hermit crab* **P. bernhardus** *twines its way in and grips with its rear legs.*
▽ *The same crab lived on quite normally, with the shell held together artificially.*

substitutes as joints of bamboo, coconut shells and even a broken oil lamp chimney. *C. diogenes* of Bermuda lives in shells that are in fact fossil or subfossil, since they belonged to a snail *Livona pica* now extinct in Bermuda. *Pylopagurus* is a hermit crab whose shell becomes encrusted with a bryozoan (moss animal). The shell is said to be dissolved leaving only the moss animal's chalky skeleton, which cloaks the crab and grows with it.

Another hermit crab *Pylocheles*, found in deep water in the Indian Ocean, lives in pieces of bamboo. Its abdomen is straight. *Xylopargus* of the West Indies lives at 600–1 200 ft in hollow cylinders of wood. The rear end of its body is shaped to make a kind of stopper. Some marine hermit crabs have less mobile homes. They live in holes in coral or sponge. This is a habit to some extent shared by lobsters and perhaps indicates the origin of the hermit crab's way of life. The coconut crab makes burrows at the bases of coconut trees and lines them with coconut husks.

Feeding on sago and coconut

Hermit crabs are mainly omnivorous scavengers, tearing up food with their smaller left claws and transferring it to their mouths. *P. bernhardus* also feeds on tiny animals and plants, tossed with sand and debris between its mouth parts with its left claw. Some other hermit crabs can filter particles from the water with bristles on the antennae. Every so often they wipe the antennae across the mouth to take the food collected. The land-living coenobites often climb bushes for plant food and may even attack young birds. The robber crab is said to hammer in the eye-holes of coconuts, but probably feeds only on coconuts already cracked open in falling from the tree. It also eats carrion, fruit and sago pith. It, too, is a climber, and can scale the trunks of sago palms and other trees. A local belief is that when the robber is up a tree it can be caught by tying a girdle of grass high up round the trunk. When the crab comes down and its body touches this it lets go, under the impression it has reached the ground, and falls and is stunned. In fact, it takes more than a fall of this kind to stun the crab.

Breeding and growth

P. bernhardus breeds through much of the year and females with 10 000–15 000 dark violet eggs attached to the swimmerets on their abdomen are to be found at most times. Such crabs, in berry as they are called when laden with eggs, come partially out of their shell from time to time and fan their swimmerets to aerate the eggs. As the larvae hatch, moulting at the same time to become zoea larvae (see p 689), the mother sits partly out of her shell and gently wipes the swimmerets with a brush of bristles on her small fourth pair of legs. The tiny shrimp-like zoea larvae shed their skins four times, growing each time, but at the fourth moult the young hermit crab first seeks a snail shell for a home. This stage lasts 4–5 days. Sexual maturity is not reached for a year or more. The sexes differ externally only in the form of the swimmerets which have differing functions, but in many the male is larger than the female.

Periodically, the growing hermit crab sheds its external skeleton. A split appears on the abdomen and the crab wriggles out of its old skin. As the hermit crab outgrows its 'home', this must be replaced with a larger one. The crab examines the new shell all over for several minutes with its claws, then, if it seems good enough and the coast seems clear, it hurriedly transfers its abdomen from the old shell to the new. Sometimes one hermit crab may try to drive another from its shell.

The 'terrestrial' hermit crabs *Coenobita* and the coconut crab *Birgus* must visit the sea to hatch their eggs, for their larvae are marine. Though the adult coconut crab does not carry a shell, the young stages coming ashore do so.

Strange partnerships

Like any hard object lying on the sea bed, the shell of a hermit crab tends to become encrusted with weed, sponges, barnacles and hydroids. Certain sea anemones, however, regularly associate with hermit crabs and form close partnerships with them. Large specimens of the common *P. bernhardus* often carry the anemone *Calliactis parasitica* on their shells, sometimes several of them. As the hermit feeds, the anemone sweeps the ground with its outstretched tentacles and gathers fragments left by the crab. The hermit crab may sometimes benefit from bits of food caught by the anemone. Another hermit crab, Prideaux's hermit crab *Pagurus prideauxi*, light reddish-brown in colour and 2 in. long, regularly carries the anemone *Adamsia palliata* which, unlike *Calliactis*, is to be found on hermit crab shells and nowhere else. The basal disc of the anemone wraps tightly around the shell, completely enclosing it. As the crustacean grows, so does the anemone, adding to the effective capacity of the shell. Thus the shell does not have to be replaced. The mouth of the anemone, in this case, lies just behind that of the hermit crab. Anemones are armed with stinging cells and these help protect the hermit crab, discouraging, for instance, the attacks of octopus and squid. *P. prideauxi* is immune to the poisons of the stinging cells which can be fatal to other hermit crabs. *Paguropsis typica* goes a stage farther than *Pagurus prideauxi* in carrying *Anemonia mammilifera* without a snail shell. Another species of hermit crab *Parapagurus pilosi-manus* has large eyes in spite of the fact that it lives in water too deep for light to penetrate: it has been suggested that it finds its way about by light from the phosphorescent anemone which cloaks it.

phylum	**Arthropoda**
class	**Crustacea**
subclass	**Malacostraca**
order	**Decapoda**
family	**Paguridae**
genus & species	***Pagurus bernhardus*** ***P. prideauxi***
family	**Coenobitidae**
genera & species	***Coenobita*** ***Birgus latro***

△ *Free food and transport in exchange for what? Hermit crabs often pick and 'plant' anemones on their backs. No satisfactory reason has yet been found.* ▽ *Brilliant East African hermit crab.*

Anthony Bannister: NHPA

Peter Hill

1025

△ *Stilt-legged sentinel: a purple heron stands guard over its nearly fledged chick.*

▽ *The egret tree: a flock of egrets forms around a roost in the Florida Everglades.*

△ *Lift-off: A goliath heron lumbers into flight. Once aloft, it is sedate and graceful.*

André Fatras

Sally Anne Thompson

Russ Kinne: Photo Res

Heron

The herons (a rather indefinite name) include bitterns, night herons and egrets. In the British Isles, 'heron' refers to the common grey heron that ranges over most of Europe and temperate tropical Asia as far south as Indonesia. It is also found in parts of Africa and on Madagascar. Closely related to it are the great blue heron of North America, the West Indies and the Galapagos Islands and the great white heron of Florida—probably no more than a local colour variation of the great blue heron. Another European species is the purple heron. It is found mainly in the south of Europe as well as many parts of Asia, Africa and Madagascar.

Some herons have characteristic long necks and legs, with long slender bills. Others, such as the North American green heron and the squacco heron of southern Europe and Africa, have comparatively short necks and legs. The powder down patches, mentioned under boatbill (p 252), are typical of herons, their relatives and a few other groups of birds such as toucans, parrots and bowerbirds. Herons have three powder down patches, one on the breast and one behind each thigh. They consist of a group of downy feathers that continually crumble into fine powder. The herons use this to absorb slime collected on their feathers after feeding on fish, first rubbing it into the plumage with the bill then scratching it out with the comb-like claws on the middle toes.

Happy landings

Herons are gregarious, nesting in colonies, often with two or more species mixing and feeding together. Their flight is slow and sedate with deliberate, ponderous wing-beats. The head is drawn back and the legs trail behind. It is a most impressive sight to see a heron land in the uppermost branches of a tree, and one which at first seems impossible. The approaching heron glides with

Feathers dry-cleaned: herons groom their plumage by dusting from powder patches (above) and combing with the serrated middle claws (below).

its legs lowered then 'backwaters' with its wings until almost hovering, and gently lowers itself onto a branch. When it has found a good foothold and is well balanced, the heron folds its wings and stands still, becoming difficult to see unless silhouetted against the sky. Much time is spent on the ground roosting with one leg raised and head sunk into its shoulders or waiting alertly for prey on a bank or in shallow water. At other times it will hunt actively, walking with long deliberate steps and neck stretched upwards with only a trace of a kink. Occasionally a heron will swim across deeper water.

Fish is the main course

Herons eat mainly fish but their diet is very varied. Water voles and frogs are probably the next most important foods of the grey herons, and others probably feed on similar aquatic animals. Crabs, prawns, shrimps, beetles, wasps, worms and snails are among the invertebrates taken and, perhaps surprisingly, quite a number of birds and mammals are attacked. These include blackbirds, moorhens, young pheasants, rats, shrews, moles and young rabbits. There is even one record of a bat being taken.

Prey is caught with a sudden thrust of the bill, but is seized in the bill rather than stabbed in the manner of darters. The short-legged herons, such as the American green heron, often dive for their food from a floating log or some other perch. Indigestible remains of the prey are disgorged and can be found on the ground beneath roosts or nests. Examination of remains gives a false idea of the heron's diet because fish bones are easily digested and are not found as commonly as remains of other prey.

Blushing suitors

Several kinds of heron and egret change colour in the breeding season, not by donning a fresh plumage like mallards but by changing colours of the 'soft parts' such as legs, bill, eyes and naked parts of the head. The iris and legs of the green heron change from yellow to orange. The base of the bill of the squacco heron changes from yellow-green to blue. The bill and legs of the grey heron and some other species sometimes flush red during moments of excitement. This is apparently caused by the same mechanism as blushing in humans; the blood vessels just under the skin swell and extra blood flows through them.

During courtship there are several quite elaborate displays either at the nest or in the air, involving movements of the neck and wings and loud snapping of the bill. The nest is usually built in a high tree but is sometimes on the ground, on cliff ledges or in reed beds. A hundred or more pairs may nest together, and several nests may be built in one tree.

The nest is a platform of twigs or reeds, collected by the male and placed in position

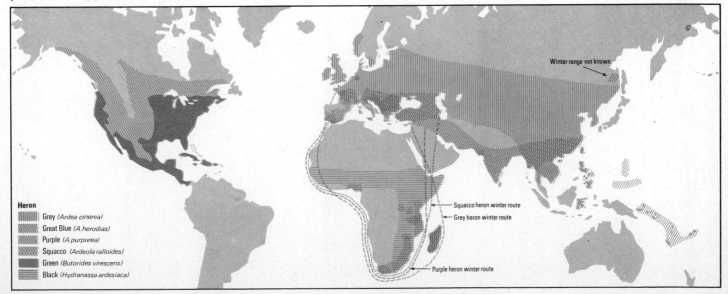

Heron
- Grey *(Ardea cinerea)*
- Great Blue *(A. herodias)*
- Purple *(A. purpurea)*
- Squacco *(Ardeola ralloides)*
- Green *(Butorides virescens)*
- Black *(Hydranassa ardesiaca)*

Winter range not known

Squacco heron winter route
Grey heron winter route

Purple heron winter route

△ *At ease: a South American white necked heron* **Ardea cocoi.**

△ *Don't dare come near! Grey heron in aggressive display.*

by the female. It is used year after year, being repaired and extended each spring until it is completely blown down by the wind. In the British Isles eggs are laid in February or March and by May or June the nests are deserted. Both parents incubate the 3−5, rarely 2−7 eggs, for about 25 days, and the young herons fly when nearly 2 months old. When they hatch the young are covered in down and stay in the nest until their feathers have grown. They then clamber out on to nearby branches, and wait, motionless, for their parents to bring food. As the parent lands, a chick grabs its bill crosswise with its own and food is taken from the parent's bill into the chick's.

Chivvied about

Adult herons are not likely to be bothered by many enemies, but their nests are robbed by carrion crows and jackdaws. It is not an unusual sight, however, to see a heron being harried by these birds or other members of the crow family, either dive-bombing the heron as it stands on the ground or a perch, or flying after it tweaking its tail. The crow family will treat other birds, their own kind and even cats in this way, apparently out of pure devilment. On one occasion in Shetland a heron was attacked by a skua. The heron was flying about 1 000 ft up and the skua, by repeated attacks, forced it to land and then lost interest. The reason for this attack is a matter of speculation, but the

skua had to change its tactics as the heron was at first able to drive it away by lunging with its bill. In mediaeval days falcons were flown at herons and apparently sometimes lost the battle by being transfixed on the heron's bill.

Clever fisherman

Animals can be conveniently divided into generalised or specialised feeders. Some of the specialised feeders may take only one kind of food, as for instance koalas feeding on eucalyptus leaves, and sometimes they will starve when surrounded by edible food if it is present in the wrong form. Frogs may starve surrounded by dead flies, for instance. Generalised feeders will eat a variety of foods, sometimes concentrating on one, sometimes on another, and this allows them to survive changing conditions which might wipe out a specialised feeder. It is now known that many animals are not quite as specialised as was thought; lions sometimes eat parts of plants for example. Similarly, herons are not limited to fish eating, but neither are they limited to lying in wait or stalking their prey. There are several instances of herons taking up new feeding habits. A line of herons has occasionally been seen to beat across a field in search of mice and in one part of England they have been seen dropping swan mussels from a height to crack open their shells on the

ground. More remarkable is the habit of the black heron that stands in shallow water with wings spread. Two reasons for this have been suggested. The wing may provide a shade so the heron can peer into the water without being blinded by glare from the sun, or fishes may be attracted to seek shelter under the shade, only to be picked off by the heron.

A green heron proved itself to be the mastermind in the heron world. It found a piece of bread, carried it to the water and dropped it in. Small fishes came to nibble the bread and were snapped up. Moreover, the heron retrieved the bread if it floated away, and later carried it to a fresh place where more fish were swimming at the surface.

class	**Aves**
order	**Ciconiiformes**
family	**Ardeidae**
genera & species	**Ardea cinerea** grey heron **A. herodias** great blue heron **A. purpurea** purple heron **Ardeola ralloides** squacco heron **Butorides virescens** green heron **Hydranassa ardesiaca** black heron others

▷ *Goliath herons* **Ardea goliath** *in the light of African sunset.*

Simon Trevor: Photo Res

Hero shrew

Sometimes called armoured shrew, the hero shrew has the most remarkable vertebral column in the whole animal kingdom. The puzzle is to know what value this can have for the animal itself—something we may learn when the two species have been better studied. At present there is only scanty information on its way of life.

Hero shrews are 8—9 in. long, of which nearly 4 in. is naked tail. On the rest of the body the fur is long, coarse and thick. Its colour is greyish with a slight tinge of buff. Otherwise a hero shrew looks like any ordinary shrew, with a tapering mobile snout, small eyes and ears half buried in the fur.

One species lives near Kampala, in Uganda, the other in the Ituri forest of the Congo, in both places on the borders of tropical rain forest.

At home under dead leaves

Hero shrews are shy and seldom seen in their home among the dense leaf litter covering the floor of the rain forest. Their movements lack the restless energy seen in most shrews and are more deliberate. They occasionally show themselves when crossing a road or path, or when they come out of the leaf litter and make a beeline for the next patch of dense shadow. They may be seen at various times during the day and have been trapped at night. So it is reasonable to suppose that they have alternating spells of activity and rest during each day, like other small mammals.

Drinking the dew

The food of hero shrews can only be surmised from the examination of the contents of a few stomachs. Nothing is known of their breeding or enemies and there are only the few notes, given here already, about their behaviour. The stomachs contained portions of adult insects, caterpillars, earthworms and very small frogs, so the diet of hero shrews is probably much the same as other shrews. Their drinking habits are of interest: one was seen to lick dew from the tufts of grass and margins of leaves. It pressed down the grass with its forefeet until it could easily reach the drops of water at the tips of the blades.

Puzzle of the backbone

By far the most fascinating aspect of the hero shrew is its backbone. Apart from a roughening of its surface the skull is like that of any other shrew, as are the limb bones, the tail bones and the ribs, and the shoulder and hip girdles. The neck bones are normal also, but just behind the shoulder the backbone rises in an arch as far as the hip girdle, several times thicker than the backbone of other shrews of similar size. This is because the vertebrae are much broadened and their surfaces ornamented with spines, ridges and bosses. As a result of these the neighbouring vertebrae interlock to give an extraordinarily strong arch. The usual explanation for this enormously strengthened arch is that it might be used

△ △ *The hero shrew, a drab little mammal.* △ *Skeleton, with the strongest backbone.*

Photographs Courtesy of the American Museum of Natural History

in turning over heavy stones as the shrew searches for the insects underneath. It has been seen to turn over large pieces of bark and pebbles, but there is little to show that the hero shrew is any more gifted in this than other shrews, or any other small mammals, such as moles. They seem to be able to turn over heavy objects out of all proportion to their weight, and they do so without such a massive backbone.

Latecomer to the textbooks

The first of the two species was discovered near Kampala in 1910 and the second came from the Ituri forest in 1913. In both cases the collectors sent the skin and the skull to the British Museum (Natural History) in London. The rest of the carcase was thrown away. This is usual for someone collecting small mammals in the field. He does not have the time or the facilities to dissect it, and probably does not take bulk preservatives. These things were especially true in the early years of the century, before Land-Rovers and airlifts were everyday methods of transport even in the jungle. Fortunately, in 1916 two American collectors in the Congo sent back 37 specimens, including one complete skeleton, to the American Museum of Natural History.

Strong-man shrew

The people of the Mangbetu tribe called the attention of the American collectors to the strength of the shrew. Whenever they

had the chance they would show to a fascinated crowd, as well as the Americans, the extraordinary resistance of the shrew to pressure. After a hubbub of invocations a man weighing 160 lb or more would stand barefoot on the shrew, balancing himself on one foot, but taking care his weight was not on the animal's head. He would hold this position for several minutes. This would squash the life out of any other shrew in a matter of seconds. Yet once the performer's foot was removed the hero shrew merely shook itself and started to walk away, to the cheers and shouts of the assembled audience.

The Mangbetu, whose name for this shrew is translated as hero shrew, are convinced that its charred body or even just its heart, when prepared by their medicine men and worn as a talisman or taken as a medicine, will endow a man with heroic qualities. Not surprisingly, they believe that such charms render them immune to serious injury from spears or arrows or from attacks by wild beasts, including elephants.

class	**Mammalia**
order	**Insectivora**
family	**Soricidae**
genus & species	*Scutisorex congicus* *S. somereni*

Herring

No single fish has had more influence on the course of human history or existed in greater abundance than the herring. It is estimated that 3 000 million are caught in the Atlantic and adjacent seas each year.

A description of the herring is rarely given on the assumption that it is familiar to everyone. It is what might well be called the typical fish, with its torpedo-shaped (fusiform) body, forked tail fin, single dorsal fin, single anal fin, pectoral fins on the breast and pelvic fins in the pelvic region, a very prototype of fish-form. Up to a foot long, its back is grey-green to golden-brown according to the colour of its background, and silvery on lower flanks and belly. Its scales have only a delicate layer of skin, and are readily rubbed off.

Shoaling fish

Herrings are pelagic fishes—that is, they spend much of their lives swimming near the surface. They feed by taking water into the mouth which passes across the gills. The plankton in it is strained off by a fine mesh-work formed by the gill-rakers and swallowed. They have small, feeble teeth. Herrings are shoaling fish living in schools, each fish spaced evenly in the school with room to swim but not to turn round. Schools are of two kinds. In the first the fishes lie with their heads level. In the second, of which herring schools are an example, the head of each fish lies opposite the middle of its neighbour's body.

Deceptive migrations

It was once thought that these vast shoals of herrings migrated from north to south, with the fishing fleets putting out from successive ports to catch them. Now we have a different picture. Herrings flourish in water temperatures of 6–15°C/43–59°F. Each year the Gulf Stream moves northeast across the Atlantic, reaching successively in summer the coasts of France, the British Isles, the Low Countries, Scandinavia and Iceland. Herrings live in colder waters. When, in summer and autumn, the warm waters withdraw, the shoals appear in the surface waters first off Shetland, then in successive areas in the North Sea and finally off the coast of Brittany in January.

We now know the herring exists in a number of races, distinguished by the number of vertebrae, speed of growth and age of sexual maturity. Also Icelandic, Norwegian, North Sea and Channel herring can be recognised, and each of these includes forms spawning at different times of the year. There are winter spawning herrings, shedding their eggs close inshore, and summer spawners laying in deeper waters. The pattern is complicated further because the different races migrate to a varying extent to spawning grounds or to feeding grounds. The race which spawns at the entrance to the Baltic remains within that area. The Norwegian race may move from southwest Norway northwards into the Arctic, into the Barents Sea, and back again.

More where they came from: about 3 000 million herring are caught every year around the Atlantic.

Fritz Siedel

Mass spawning

What happens to herrings when they are in deeper waters is uncertain. Possibly the schools are more spread out. The schools are most compact when they are made up of young fishes and when adults are coming together for spawning. The act of spawning is random, the females shedding their eggs, the males shedding their milt to fertilize the eggs, the parents then moving on and paying no more attention to them. Spawning appears to be accompanied by some excited swimming about but there seems to be no courtship. The eggs, $\frac{1}{25}$ in. diameter, are laid in sticky clumps which are heavier than sea water and sink to the bottom, coming to rest on a shingly sea bed. Only 21 000–47 000 are laid by each female, a very small number compared with the millions laid by some other marine fishes. This is a sure sign that they are relatively immune from attack, lying on the shingle beds, as compared with floating eggs.

The eggs hatch in 8–9 days at temperatures between 11°–14°C/52°–58°F but take 47 days at 0°C/32°F, while at lower temperatures they fail altogether. The larvae, $\frac{1}{4}$ in. long when hatched, are transparent and still carry the remains of the yolk sac. They have no mouth or gills and only a single fin down the middle of the back and round the rear end. Development is rapid, however, and in a month the baby fish may be $\frac{2}{5}$ in. long and looking almost like its parents. The growth rate then begins to slow down, the young fish being at most 2 in.

long, usually much less, by the end of the year. Maturity is reached in 4–5 years

They founded cities . . .

The fishing grounds of the northern hemisphere, as well as supplying nations with food, have greatly influenced their history. The herring is an outstanding example. It has been suggested that wherever the shoals of herrings came in towards the coast of Norway there sprang up a village. The same seems to have been true for Scotland and Newfoundland, and for Alaska, Japan and Siberia with respect to the Pacific herring. The villages may now have become towns, and in addition to these there are towns that were deliberately founded to cater for the fishing. Charlemagne, in 809 AD, founded Hamburg as a herring port. Viking descendants, the Normans, established Ostend, Dunkirk, Etaples, Dieppe and Fécamp for the same purpose: Fécamp is said to be derived from the Viking name *Fisk havn*, the fish harbour.

. . . and caused wars

Along the coast of North Prussia, and extending to Norway and Belgium, were many free cities and small states carrying on general trade which were compelled to supply armed escorts for their merchandise, especially against pirates. In the 13th century they banded together to sail their great merchant fleets in convoy under protection. This co-operative group became known as the Hanseatic League, with Lübeck as head-

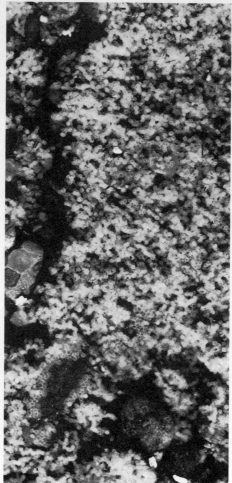

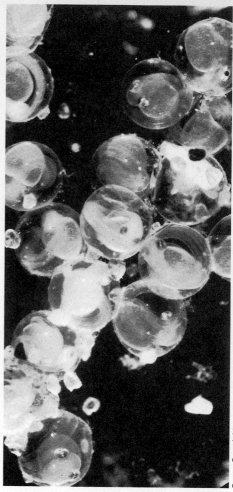

Crown Copyright

quarters. Their ships carried herrings from the Baltic ports and brought back wool, timber, wine and other merchandise. The herrings were fished by Danes off the south coast of Sweden, but the curing and exporting were the concern of merchants in the north German towns. The League monopolised almost the whole of the export trade of Europe and for two centuries was a dominating influence in northern Europe.

Then suddenly the stocks of herring in the Baltic disappeared, the result it was supposed of some natural catastrophe, now believed to have been a lowering of the temperature. In any event the stocks never recovered. But about this same time the Dutch had begun to export salted herrings fished in English waters. This new fishery prospered and in 1610 Sir Walter Raleigh estimated that the Dutch employed 3 000 ships and 50 000 people in their herring industry. The Dutch fishing led to friction with England who wanted to extract a tribute for herrings taken in her waters, and the friction led also to the founding of the Royal Navy in Stuart times and to the 1652-4 war in which England wrested sea power from Holland.

The vital herring

In the 19th century friction arose between the fishermen of New England and those of Newfoundland over the fishing on the Grand Banks, which the Newfoundlanders regarded as their natural rights. In 1877, under the Halifax Commission Treaty, the

Some of the herring family, like the Pacific herring, lay their sticky eggs around any suitable rock or plant on the seabed (left). Others, like the Atlantic herring, let their eggs sink from the spawning levels to the shingle sea floor (above) where they are quite well camouflaged. The babies within develop quickly; the ones at right are about halfway.

Herring spawning grounds
○ spring ● autumn & winter

United States paid Great Britain 5½ million dollars for their fishermen to be able to fish for herring within the 3-mile limit off the Gulf of St Lawrence and Newfoundland. Nevertheless, one Sunday morning in Fortune Bay, the Newfoundland fishermen cut the seines of two of the New England schooners, so the entire catch was lost; another New England schooner saved its catch only by threatening to shoot, and the rest of the fleet sailed for home. The incident is known merely as the Fortune Bay Riot, but it is yet another example of the constantly recurring friction over fishing.

Even the Russo-Japanese war of 1902 was inspired by a Japanese claim to the herrings off the Russian territory of Sakhalin Island. More recently there has been the friction between British trawlers and the Icelandic gunboats. Iceland's anxieties over her fishing can be appreciated when it is recalled that she employs nearly 7 000 fishermen and that 95% of her exports are fish products.

class	**Pisces**
order	**Clupeiformes**
family	**Clupeidae**
genus & species	***Clupea harengus***

Barnaby's

Seeking what they may devour: herring gulls, burly, heavy-billed scavengers of the seashore.

Herring gull

The herring gull is one of the commonest gulls around the shores of the British Isles where it can be seen perching along the sea front, fighting noisily over refuse or following fishing boats in the hope of an easy meal. It is quickly distinguished from other gulls by its size and by its grey back and wings. The wingtips are black with spots of white, the legs flesh-coloured and the bill yellow with a red spot on the tip. Young herring gulls are mottled brown; as they grow older the mottling diminishes until, at 4 years, they reach adult plumage.

Herring gulls live in northwestern Europe, around the coasts of the British Isles, the Faeroes and eastern Iceland and on the Continent from Brittany to northern Finland, including the Baltic coast. In North America they breed to the north of a line running approximately from the Great Lakes to the borders of Alaska. Iceland was colonised by herring gulls in 1927 and Spitsbergen in 1950. This spread is probably due to the slow warming that is taking place in the North Atlantic.

More rubbish, more food, more gulls

The herring gull has always been common but especially in the last 20 years its numbers have increased greatly. This is probably because of the increased amount of food in the form of edible refuse at rubbish dumps and offal at fishing ports. Some colonies number 20 000 pairs. Herring gulls have also begun to breed inland, nesting by lakes or even on buildings.

Scavengers and ruthless pirates

Although gulls are basically fish eaters many of them have made use of other sources of food. Herring gulls have become scavengers and hunters as well as fishers. They feed on any edible garbage, a very wide variety of animals and some seeds and roots. Herring gulls are a scourge of many other birds nesting in the open around coasts because they plunder nests for eggs and chicks. They also take adult shearwaters and other gulls, as well as some land animals such as shrews, rabbits, frogs and even adders. It is difficult to know, however, whether full-grown individuals are captured alive or taken as carrion. The gulls probably concentrate their attacks on weakened and wounded individuals.

The shore is a favourite feeding ground for herring gulls. They search among rocks and in pools for shellfish and crustaceans. Shellfish such as mussels that can protect themselves by closing up, unlike rock-hugging limpets, are carried into the air and dropped so the shell is broken. This seems very clever but the gulls do not choose where to drop them. They can be seen flying up 20 ft or so repeatedly dropping shells onto soft sand. It is only when the shells drop onto rocks, quite by chance, that the method is successful.

Dive-bomber camouflage

When fishing at sea herring gulls, like many of their relatives, catch their prey by plunge-diving, dropping into the water from a few feet above with wings half folded. The gulls very rarely submerge completely, usually immersing only head and neck or part of the body. This means that they must catch the fishes they are aiming at first time or else they will escape. Experiments at Oxford University have shown that the white plumage of a herring gull is an advantage in this respect. By rolling models down a slope towards an aquarium it was shown that the fish in the aquarium reacted more quickly to a dark model. They were able to flee several inches farther before the model struck the water if it was dark than if it was white. Observations in the North Sea suggest that this is important in practice. Adult herring gulls are found mainly out to sea where they feed by plunge-diving. The juveniles with their dark plumage stay near the shore feeding on refuse and shore creatures.

Keeping the eggs together

Herring gulls nest in colonies on cliffs or small islands or among sand dunes. Occasionally colonies can be found inland, by lakes, in bogs or on buildings. Each pair has a small territory surrounding their nest of grass, seaweed or other plants. Each gull returns regularly to the same territory with the same mate. They spend the winter away from the colony, then in early spring they return to claim their territories and a certain

Herring gull— or garbage gull?

Left: Beady-eyed herring gull at nest shows its yellow bill with the distinctive red spot, which acts as a 'target' for the feeding chicks to peck at. They remain faithful to their mates and to their nesting territory, returning regularly to reclaim it after every winter.
Below: A typical herring gull colony. They nest on cliffs, small islands, or among sand dunes, but are not averse to breeding inland.
Right: Professional beachcombers at work. These herring gulls are giving a garbage-ridden stretch of shoreline an expert working-over. Any increase of rubbish-tipping means more food for herring gulls—and the result is more herring gulls.
Below right: Herring gull chick, a huge-footed puff-ball of indignation 3 weeks old.
Far right: Bending the rules—herring gull **Larus argentatus** *mated with a lesser black-backed gull* **Larus fuscus.** *This hybridisation, the result of egg-changing experiments, occurs only very rarely in the wild, despite the fact that the ranges of both gulls overlap.*

André Fatras

JLS Dubois: Jacana

amount of fighting takes place until they have settled down. Courtship gets under way, either renewing old ties or finding a new mate if the old one has died.

After the nest is built, three brown eggs with blackish blotches are laid. Both sexes incubate them, taking turns of a few hours each for about 26 days. In common with many birds that nest on the ground, herring gulls will retrieve their eggs if they are knocked out of the nest. This is quite easy to demonstrate by putting one of the eggs just outside the nest. The gull returns and settles down on the nest, but it realises something is wrong. It stands up again and looks at the eggs and shuffles them about. Eventually it leans forward, hooks its bill over the stray egg and draws it into the nest — and all is well.

Feeding-aids for chicks and parents
The chicks are brooded in the nest at intervals while they are young, but from a very early age they can run about the territory. The parents bring food back to them. At first they regurgitate it and hold small pieces in the tip of the bill for the chicks to peck at. Later, food is dropped to the ground and the chicks pick pieces off for themselves. Herring gulls, as well as other gulls, terns and skuas, are stimulated to feed their chicks by the latter pecking at their bills. In the herring gull, the chicks aim at the red patch on the bill and it has been shown that in all these birds the chicks are specially sensitive to red, so the red spot is acting as a 'target' for the chick to peck at.

Parent gulls defend their chicks vigorously, flying at intruders to scare them away and giving alarm calls which alert the chicks and send them scurrying to shelter. The chicks start to fly when 6 weeks old but take

a few days to learn efficient take-off and landing. A short time later, they leave the colony, although they will stay with their parents for a little time.

Around the world
The lesser black-backed gull lives around the coasts of Europe and across Asia. It is very similar to the herring gull except that back and wings are black and the legs are yellow. Also, the herring gull has a ring of yellow flesh around the eye, while the lesser black-backed gull has a vermilion eye ring. These differences seem to be sufficient to class the two as separate species but, like the carrion and hooded crows (p 583) that used to be considered separate species, herring gulls and lesser black-backed gulls occasionally interbreed. In fact, they are members of what is called a ring species. Around the northern hemisphere there are several races of herring gull. From the original home in eastern Siberia the population has spread through North America in one direction and through Asia and Europe in the other direction. Each of the two races is sufficiently like its neighbours to interbreed freely with them, but the two streams have diverged and where they meet and overlap in northwestern Europe as the herring gull and lesser black-backed gull interbreeding is very rare. But it is quite possible; they have interbred and the offspring are fertile, so by definition they are of the same species. It is still usual, however, to assign them to separate species.

In normal circumstances, however, herring gulls and lesser black-backed gulls do not interbreed. We have already seen how in fruit flies (p 830) and deer mice (p 623) there are mechanisms keeping species from

interbreeding. The two gulls also have isolating mechanisms. They nest together in mixed colonies but are kept in practical isolation by their behaviour. The courtship calls and displays of the males are somewhat different so it is likely that the females are able to select the right mate, aided by differences in wing and eye ring colour.

Apart from being a well-known seaside bird, the herring gull has probably been studied in more detail than any other bird. In 1953 Niko Tinbergen published *The Herring Gull's World,* in which experiments on courtship, nesting and chick behaviour were described. These experiments formed much of the basis of the modern study of animal behaviour. They showed how the gulls were reacting to certain features of their environment or signals from their fellows called sign stimuli. The sign stimuli were as fixed as road signs, and the reactions of the gulls to them automatic.

Since *The Herring Gull's World* was published much more work has been done on herring gulls, some of it extending the work already begun, while other experiments and observations investigated other departments of the herring gull's life. This is the work which is summarised here. Similar work has been carried out on other species of gulls and their relatives to build up a more complete picture of their lives and the forces that mould them.

class	**Aves**
order	**Charadriiformes**
family	**Laridae**
genus & species	***Larus argentatus*** herring gull ***L. fuscus*** lesser black-backed gull

Ace scavengers in action: a gang of herring gulls comb the waterline for floating refuse, dead marine animals and fish — and indeed for any small invertebrate foolish enough to show itself — when it's a question of getting a meal, all is grist to their mill.

Horizontal hide-and-seek: a distrustful-looking Amazon river turtle pulls its head in with a sideways bend of its neck. Compared with the cryptodire turtles' method—withdrawal in the orthodox vertical fashion—hidden-necked turtles' technique is far more primitive.

Hidden-necked turtle

When a tortoise or terrapin pulls its head into the shelter of its shell its neck usually bends vertically. The hidden-necked (or side-necked) turtles, however, bend their necks horizontally. Apart from this they are of interest because of the way they are distributed, and there is a special interest in the history of the South American species.

There are three kinds of hidden-necked turtles: two in Africa and one in South America that turns up again in distant Madagascar. The half-a-dozen or so African species are usually grouped under two names: pelomedusas and box turtles. After that the species themselves are apt to be given different names in different places. For example, the pelomedusa is also called helmeted terrapin and water tortoise. The box turtles of Africa have the front part of the underside of the shell (plastron) hinged so it can be drawn up to shut the head in once it is withdrawn.

Here we will be concentrating on two species: the Amazon river turtle, also living in the Orinoco, and the African water tortoise.

Breeding will tell

Known in the Orinoco basin of Venezuela as the *arrau*, the female Amazon turtle reaches 3 ft long, while the smaller, almost circular male grows to a diameter of 1½ ft. Most females weigh about 50 lb, but weights of up to 130 lb have been recorded. These turtles live on a variety of animal food, taking also some plant food, but little is known of their habits. They behave generally as other turtles do, apart from their breeding. This is remarkably like that of marine turtles, such as the green turtle (p 948). In early February, as the dry season begins, the waters drop, exposing sandbanks and islands in mid-river. The turtles gather in the water around the sandbanks in their thousands, and they mate in the water. Some have travelled 100 miles to a suitable sandbank area. After mating, the males leave, while the females land at night to lay.

Millions of sand-packed eggs

Each of the thousands of females fairly closely packed on the sand digs a pit, 3 ft wide and 2 ft deep, with a smaller pit at its base in which the eggs are deposited. The larger pit is dug with all four legs, the smaller one with hindlegs only. Into it up to 150 eggs (average 80), nearly 2 in. diameter and soft-shelled, are laid. After this the female fills in the pit, disturbs the sand all around masking the actual site, and leaves. Night after night thousands more females arrive to lay. Six weeks later the 2 in. hatchlings dig their way up out of the sand, to run the gauntlet of vultures, storks and ibis. Those that reach the water face another hazard from crocodiles and predatory fishes.

Unwanted tortoise

The African water tortoise is up to 13 in. long and nearly 10 in. across. Its back is a mottled greenish-brown. The turtle, found over Africa, south of the Sahara, has earned a bad reputation in South Africa, and possibly in other parts, for its repulsive smell and its attacks on ducklings. It also steals bait from anglers' hooks. The odour comes from four glands, one under each leg, which give out an evil-smelling liquid, said to be especially objectionable to horses, as well as humans. The tortoise's food is almost entirely animal, although it readily feeds on plants. It runs fast on land and it swims even faster, so that ducklings are highly vulnerable, being seized by a leg, dragged underwater and consumed when drowned.

There is nothing spectacular in its breeding. The female about to lay comes on land, selects a site, releases a quantity of urine on the ground and puddles the mud with her feet. She repeats this ejection of urine several times until a stiff mud is formed, making digging easier. Then, using the leading edge of her plastron as a bulldozer, and pushing with her hindlegs, she digs a hole 4 in. across at the bottom of which she excavates a smaller chamber. Into this she lays about a score of oval, soft-shelled eggs, 1½ in. long by ¾ in. across. The shell membrane later hardens. When the hatchlings burrow up to the surface, they also have to face the threat posed by hammerheads, herons and other birds waiting for them.

A mixed family?

Although the African and the South American species are placed in the same family it is tempting to think they cannot be closely related. The African water tortoise makes the same kind of nest as a land tortoise, and behaves in the same way. The South American river turtle behaves in every way like the marine turtles, so one could imagine its ancestors living in the sea and gradually moving to large rivers.

Give and take

As far back as records go, the local people in the Amazon and Orinoco basins have used the turtle eggs as food. When Henry Batès wrote his *Naturalist on the Amazons* a century ago he described how the eggs were collected. The people were forbidden by law to take eggs before all the female turtles had left the islands. Then, at a given signal, all began digging in the sand. Bates estimated that 48 million eggs were gathered each year. The local people also killed and ate the adults as well as large numbers of hatchlings. The result was that even then the numbers seemed to be dwindling. Recently Dr Janis Arose, Venezuelan zoologist, has described similar scenes on the Orinoco and

Jane Burton: Photo Res

expressed fears for the survival of the turtles. But it is interesting to note that the crocodiles which formerly preyed on the hatchling turtles have been much reduced in numbers because of the market for crocodile skins for leather. Moreover, jaguars, which eat the adults, are less numerous than they were. These two things may perhaps go some way to counterbalancing the slaughter of the turtles by human beings.

class	**Reptilia**
order	**Chelonia**
family	**Pelomedusidae**
genera & species	***Pelomedusa subrufa*** *African water tortoise* ***Podocnemis expansa*** *Amazon river turtle*

△ *In the swim: a South American hidden-necked turtle under way. This genus,* **Podocnemis,** *is based in tropical South America—but it also crops up in faraway Madagascar. The most probable reason for this puzzling distribution is that the ancestral marine turtles were widely dispersed through the shallow coastal seas; some of them entered the rivers to become the ancestors of modern freshwater turtles, leaving the sea to other families. These freshwater types grow quite large: the biggest of the Amazon river turtles can reach a shell length of 30 in.*

▽ *African water tortoise sunning itself on a log. Unlike the Amazon river turtles, these rarely have a shell length bigger than 12 in. Although mostly aquatic they take readily to land, and are found all over central and southern Africa wherever they can be near to water. Mainly carnivorous, they take some plant food.*

MJ Coe

Hillstream fish

Fishes of several different families manage to live in mountain torrents where water cascades down, in some places carrying boulders several feet across as if they were pebbles. Such fishes are known collectively as hillstream fishes and here we examine what they need in order to survive, and what are the advantages of living in such inhospitable surroundings. Together they give a wonderful example of animals specially adapted to an unusual environment as well as an instance of convergent evolution.

The families represented include catfishes, loaches, carps and suckers and they are found mainly in three regions: in the Andes, in southern and southeast Asia and the Malay Archipelago.

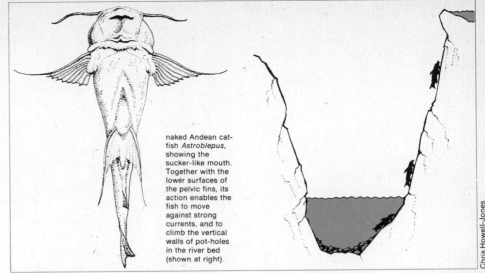

naked Andean catfish *Astroblepus*, showing the sucker-like mouth. Together with the lower surfaces of the pelvic fins, its action enables the fish to move against strong currents, and to climb the vertical walls of pot-holes in the river bed (shown at right).

Chris Howell-Jones

△ *Underside of a typical hillstream fish.*

▽ *Bottom-hugger — mailed catfish* **Plecostomus**.

John H Tashjian at Steinhart Aquarium

Life in the torrents

An obvious advantage for any animal living in a harsh environment is that it will have few natural enemies. To secure this advantage hillstream fishes must be adapted to surviving the rush of water, unusual features in the stream bed such as potholes and large boulders, and a limited supply of food. The first need of a hillstream fish is to be able to cling to a solid support and let the torrent of water slide over its body without dislodging it. So most of them are flattened, especially on the underside, and some species are almost leaf-like. The exceptions are the loaches, which have narrow cylindrical bodies and can creep into crevices or spaces under the rocks. Because of the absence of enemies there is no need for armour or defensive spines, and even the scales normally covering a fish's body are small, few in number or absent altogether. A striking example is seen in the catfish *Astroblepus* of the Andes. Its closest relatives are the armoured catfishes (p 85) which are coated with heavy scales, whereas *Astroblepus* has a naked skin.

Clinging to life

All hillstream fishes have small eyes and this it is believed is a protection against the strong light that reaches them through the crystal-clear water. The snout is broad and flat, either because in some species the mouth serves as a sucker or because it is used to crop the thin layer of small green algae coating the rocks. But the most important adaptations are those used for clinging. In some of the Asiatic catfishes the lower surface, especially on the chest, is puckered into ridges which prevent the fish slipping. In some carps the outer rays of the paired fins are thickened, sometimes with cushion-like pads of skin for giving a better hold. In many there is a sucker on the chest, a rounded pad-like centre surrounded by a flap of skin. Loaches and suckers actually use the mouth, with fleshy lips forming the rim of the sucker. The catfishes of the Andes also have a sucker mouth and they can grip with their pelvic fins. By using these alternately the fish can creep along the bottom against a rapid current or climb the vertical sides of a pothole.

All hillstream fishes have a particularly muscular tail, especially useful in darting rapidly from one stone to another across a rapid current. The Andean catfishes exploit this in their climbing, the tail giving a strong thrust forward.

Holding their breath

Fishes breathe by taking water in through the mouth, passing it across the gills and out through the gill-opening. Any fish holding on, using its mouth as a sucker, or feeding on the algal slime on rocks, using its mouth rather like a vacuum cleaner, may have difficulty in breathing. Hillstream fishes have solved the problem in several ways. For example, a Malayan carp *Gyrinocheilus* and several catfishes have the gill-opening divided into two so water flows in through one half and out through the other. In others the problem is solved by suspending their breathing for long periods on end. They are the better able to do this because the amount of oxygen in shallow agitated waters is always high. Also, the waters are cold, and fishes use less oxygen at low temperatures.

A diet of mud

Even the mouth has had to undergo changes. The broad flat snout already mentioned means the mouth is broad and almost slit-like. Many hillstream fishes have no teeth. Instead the jaws have sharp cutting edges, sometimes covered with a strong horny sheath. Where there are teeth these are minute and arranged in bands, almost file-like. The Malay carp already mentioned eats mud, using its mouth not only as a sucker for clinging to rocks but for sucking in mud. There is so little food value in the mud that the carp must take in large quantities — and so its coiled intestine is 14 times its own length.

All for survival

The three basic aims of any living creature are to find food, to seek protection from enemies and to reproduce its kind. In seeking protection many species at every level of the animal scale have made use of inhospitable places. This is what the hillstream fishes have done, but there are many other examples. We find them also in human communities. The pygmy hunters of the Ituri forest in the Congo have found refuge in the dense jungle. The Bushmen of South Africa eke out a living in the harsh Kalahari desert. The Ainu, the aboriginals of Japan, took to the mountains. Until modern civilization brought unparalleled means of entering into and exploring, as well as exploiting, almost any kind of terrain, dense forests, deserts and high mountains gave those hardy tribes, capable of adapting to them, security from persecution and freedom from competition for food, meagre though the food supply may be. Hillstream fishes have found a haven in watery counterpart to these land conditions.

class	**Pisces**	
order	**Cypriniformes**	
families	**Cyprinidae, Cobitidae, Homalopteridae**	
order	**Siluriformes**	
family	**Loricariidae**	

Himalayan black bear

This is one of the five species of black bear, the others being the American, spectacled, sloth and Malayan sun bears. Also known as the moon bear, it has a white crescent or new moon on its chest.

The Himalayan bear is up to 6½ ft long with a 3in. tail, and weighs up to 265 lb. The fur is short and smooth without underfur; it is thin in summer and thick in winter, especially on the shoulders where it is extra long, giving the appearance of a hump. The ears are larger than in other bears and covered with long hair. In addition to the white chest patch, there is a small white patch on the chin and the upper lip is sometimes whitish. The nose is reddish-brown. The black claws are short.

This bear ranges from northern Persia through the Himalayas to northern Laos, North Vietnam and Hainan in the south, throughout China to Siberia, Korea and Formosa in the north. There is a distinct race on Kyushu, Japan.

▷ **Selenarctos thibetanus** rears up in a threatening pose. Could frightened reports of sightings like this be a basis for the legend of the 'Abominable Snowman', the dreaded yeti? Himalayan black bears are more aggressive than the bears of the Old World; apart from raids on domestic animals, they occasionally kill men. **Selenarctos** means 'moon bear', and the 'crescent moon' on this bear's chest shows up plainly.

▷▽ Cooling off—a Himalayan black bear enjoys a quiet wallow. Like other bears, this species has no hesitation in taking to water and is a ready swimmer.

▷▷ A surly zoo inmate glowers at the camera. The normal colour is black, apart from the white markings on chest and chin, but some are brown or reddish-brown.

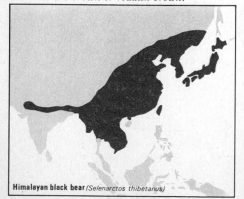

Himalayan black bear (Selenarctos thibetanus)

Okapia

A Markowitz

Neighbours on nodding terms

The Himalayan black bear lives in forest or brush up to 11 000 ft in summer and 4 500 ft or lower in winter. It is a good climber and swims well. Like other bears it is solitary, individuals having little to do with each other except to mate. Bears do not hold territories; they occupy a home range which is not an area of ground with a perimeter but a number of spots visited regularly for feeding, drinking, resting or sunning, these places being linked by well-trodden paths. The home ranges of two or more bears may overlap each other, so bears often pass their fellows but ignore them. It seems, however, that they recognize their neighbours even though they disregard them. The paths and chosen places in a home range are marked by scratchings on trees, and such posts are further marked by the bear chewing the bark, urinating on it and rubbing its neck glands on it. The 'signposts' thus can be recognized both by sight and smell.

In summer the Himalayan black bear makes nests of sticks in trees in which to rest. In winter it makes a bed of sticks on the snow for resting or for basking. It may hibernate for short periods during severe weather, but normally it does not hibernate.

Undeserved reputation for ferocity?

It is mainly vegetarian, feeding on berries, nuts, roots, ants and honey, and it is apt to raid crops of maize, rice, buckwheat, melons, fruit and nuts. Whether all individuals are flesheaters is not certain; some are known to have killed lambs as well as calves and ponies and the Himalayan black bear is generally regarded as one of the main enemies of the Kashmir stag, killing the young. It also has the reputation of being less afraid of men than most bears and readily attacking, even killing, people if provoked. It has the curious trick of rolling downhill in a ball.

The reputation of all bears for being treacherous is challenged by Peter Krott, writing in *Natural History* for 1962. He kept bears as pets and suggests the following explanation for people being mauled or lacerated by apparently tame bears. Unlike most carnivores the mother bear does not present food to her offspring. She suckles them but when they are at heel they seek their own food, much of which is moving prey, such as small rodents or insects, which they grab with their claws. When someone tries to hand-feed a bear, that person is introducing the animal to a wholly unnatural situation. It reacts as it would to moving prey, cutting loose with its claws. This may not be the whole story of bear attacks but Krott puts forward a convincing argument against offering bears food with the hand.

Another reason put forward to explain the bear's alleged ferocity is that being solitary the animal has no need of facial expressions to communicate with its fellows. About the only thing it does is to show the whites of its eyes when about to attack. This conflicts with the views expressed by Krott who claims that even his children, aged 6 and 4 years, soon learned to read the pet bear's facial expression from the look in its eyes and the movements of its mobile nose.

Quick-growing infants

The usual litter is of two cubs born (in a winter den) in January or February, blind and no bigger than a rat. After leaving the den they follow the mother, sometimes until after the next litter is born. They grow rapidly at first but do not reach maturity until 3 years old.

Bear-worship and folk medicine

Their main enemy is man; the Chinese in the past have prized their flesh and bones for supposed medicinal properties. The aboriginal Ainu, of Japan, used the pelt for clothing and ate the flesh. They also worshipped the bear, which figured in their religious festivals, bear victims being killed in a somewhat cruel and barbaric ritual.

Thumb-sucking bears

Himalayan black bears are commonly kept in zoos. In captivity they have been seen to hold their paws out in front as if begging for alms and then to lick the pads continuously until they are covered with a thick creamy paste of saliva. At the same time they make a deep throaty noise, a sort of purr in the throat. There have been several explanations put forward to account for this. The first is that it is a form of bear fever. Another is that the bears obtain nourishment from the paws. The third is that there are glands on the undersides of the paws from which something can be obtained which assists digestion. The fourth is that when bears are doing this they are in fact talking to each other. It seems, however, that not all bears do this. In the wild during hibernation, some bears have been seen lying and sucking one paw. It is this largely that has given rise to the suggestion that paw-licking is a way of obtaining nourishment during a period of fasting. It is more likely to be a form of thumb-sucking, perhaps a sign of contentment. Zoo bears, however, actually suck the pads, or lick them vigorously, and this seems to be a different form of thumb-sucking, arising from sheer boredom as a result of captivity.

class	**Mammalia**
order	**Carnivora**
family	**Ursidae**
genus & species	***Selenarctos thibetanus***

◁ *Not a yawn, but a gape of defiance.*

△ *Hippos' delight: a floating pasture with water to wallow in, abundant food, and attendant egrets.*

Hippopotamus

Distantly related to the pigs, the hippopotamus rivals the great Indian rhinoceros as the second largest living land animal. Up to 14 ft long and 4 ft 10 in at the shoulder it weighs up to 4 tons. The enormous body is supported on short pillar-like legs, each with four toes ending in hoof-like nails, placed well apart. A hippo trail in swamps shows as two deep ruts made by the feet with a dip in the middle made by the belly. The eyes are raised on top of the large flattish head, the ears are small and the nostrils slit-like and high up on the muzzle. The body is hairless except for sparse bristles on the muzzle, inside the ears and on the tip of the short tail. There is a thick layer of fat under the skin and there are pores in the skin which give out an oily pink fluid, known as pink sweat. This lubricates the skin. The mouth is armed with large canine tusks; these average 2½ ft long but may be over 5 ft long including the long root embedded in the gums.

Once numerous in rivers throughout Africa, the hippopotamus is now extinct north of Khartoum and south of the Zambezi river, except in a few protected areas such as the Kruger National Park.

The pygmy hippopotamus, a separate species, lives in Liberia, Sierra Leone and parts of southern Nigeria in forest streams. It is 5 ft long, 2 ft 8 in. at the shoulder and weighs up to 600 lb. Its head is smaller in proportion to the body, and it lives singly or in pairs.

Rulebook of the river-horse

The name means literally river-horse and the hippopotamus spends most of its time in water, but comes on land to feed, mainly at night. It can remain submerged for up to 4½ minutes and spends the day basking lethargically on a sandbar, or lazing in the water with little more than ears, eyes and nostrils showing above water, at most with its back and upper part of the head exposed. Where heavily persecuted, hippopotamuses keep to reed beds. Each group, sometimes spoken of as a school, numbers around 20–100 and its territory is made up of a central crèche occupied by females and juveniles with separate areas, known as refuges, around its perimeter each occupied by an adult male. The crèche is on a sandbar in midstream or on a raised bank of the river or lake. Special paths lead from the males' refuges to the feeding grounds, each male marking his own path with his dung. The females have their own paths but are less exclusive.

The organisation of the territories is preserved by rules of behaviour which, in some of their aspects, resemble rules of committees. Outside the breeding season a female may pay a social call on a male and he may return this, but on the female's terms. He must enter the crèche with no sign of aggression and should one of the females rise on her feet he must lie down. Only when she lies down again may he rise. A male failing to observe these rules will be driven out by the adult females attacking him *en masse*.

Matriarch hippos

It was long thought that a hippopotamus school was led by the oldest male. It is in fact a matriarchy. For example, young males, on leaving the crèche, are forced to take up a refuge beyond the ring of refuges lying on the perimeter of the crèche. From there each must win his way to an inner refuge, which entitles him to mate with one of the females, by fighting. Should a young male be over-persecuted by the senior males he can re-enter the crèche for sanctuary, protected by the combined weight of the females.

The characteristic yawning has nothing to do with sleep. It is an aggressive gesture, a preliminary challenge to fight. Combats are vigorous, the two contestants rearing up out of the water, enormous mouths wide open, seeking to deliver slashing cuts with the long tusks. Frightful gashes are inflicted and a wounded hippo falling back into water screams with pain, but the wounds quickly heal. The aim of the fighting is for one hippo to break a foreleg of his opponent. This is fatal because the animal can no longer walk on land to feed.

Nightly wanderings

Hippos feed mostly at night, coming on land to eat mainly grass. During one night an individual may wander anything up to 20 miles but usually does not venture far from water. Hippos have been known to wander through the outskirts of large towns at times, and two surprised just before dawn by a motorist entering Nairobi showed him they could run at 30 mph.

Babies in nursery school

When in season the female goes out to choose her mate and he must treat her with deference as she enters his refuge. The baby is born 210–255 days later. It is 3 ft long, 1½ ft high and 60 lb weight. Birth may take place in water but normally it is on land, the mother preparing a bed of trampled reeds. The baby can walk, run or swim 5 minutes after birth. Outside the crèche

'I shoot the hippopotamus with bullets made of platinum . . .

Below: Just cruising along . . . the hippo may be a massive tank of an animal, but it certainly has the knack of drifting quietly through glass-calm water with the minimum of fuss. Notice how nostrils, eyes and ears are all above the water.

Bottom: A mournful-looking pygmy hippo **Choeropsis liberiensis,** *from West Africa. Its well-oiled look is due to the secretion of a clear, viscous material through its skin pores. When frightened, the pygmy hippo prefers to head for* *the undergrowth, whereas the big hippos invariably seek safety in water. The pygmy hippo is a shy beast, and is therefore hard to find. Normally found singly or in pairs, it is not usually vicious except when disturbed.*

Mondadori Press

Carlo Bevilacqua

. . . because if I use leaden ones his hide is sure to flatten 'em.' (Hilaire Belloc)

Below left: The hippo's coppery-red tint comes, from light reflections off beads of red-tinted moisture exuded by skin glands—the basis of the statement that the hippo 'sweats blood'. Nostrils and ears are closed when submerging.

Below right: 'I name this ship . . .'—a hippo lumbers into the water in Murchison Falls National Park. The normal period for their submarine act is from 3 to 5 minutes, but they can stay under water for nearly 30 minutes.

Bottom: On the waterfront—like an Easter Day parade. A trio of hippos in single file moves ponderously through a mixed throng of cormorants, pelicans and gulls, with a hippo youngster stepping out in the lead.

KB Newman

Des Bartlett: Photo Res

Okapia

'So follow me, follow — down to the hollow — and there let us wallow in glo-o-orious mud.' A classic picture of a hippo taking time out in the best Flanders and Swann tradition! Like rhinoceroses, hippos often cool off in this glutinous way, the ultimate in mud-pack beauty treatment.

Popperfoto

the organisation of the school is dependent on fighting and the females educate the young accordingly. This is one of the few instances of deliberate teaching in the animal kingdom. In a short while after its birth the baby hippo is taken on land for walks, not along the usual paths used when going to pasture but in a random promenade. The youngster must walk level with the mother's neck presumably so she can keep an eye on it. If the mother quickens her pace, the baby must do the same. If she stops, it must stop. In water the baby must swim level with her shoulder. On land the lighter female is more agile than the male, so she can defend her baby without difficulty. In the water the larger male, with his longer tusks, has the advantage, so the baby must be where the mother can quickly interpose her own body to protect her offspring from an aggressive male. Later, when she takes it to pasture, the baby must walk at heel, and if she has more than one youngster with her, which can happen because her offspring stay with her for several years, they walk behind her in order of precedence, the elder bringing up the rear.

Obedience, or else . . .
The youngsters must show strict obedience, and the penalty for failing to do so is punishment, the mother lashing the erring youngster with her head, often rolling it over and over. She may even slash it with her tusks. The punishment continues until the youngster cowers in submission, when the mother licks and caresses it.

Babysitting was not invented by the human race: hippos brought it to a fine art long ago. If a female leaves the crèche for feeding or mating she places her youngster in charge of another female, who may already have several others under her supervision. The way for this is made easy, for hippo mothers with young of similar age tend to keep together in the crèche.

The young hippos play with others of similar age, the young females together playing a form of hide-and-seek or rolling over in the water with stiff legs. The young males play together but they indulge in mock fights in addition to the other games.

Few enemies for the hippo
Hippos have few enemies apart from man, the most important being the lion which may occasionally spring on the back of a hippo on land, raking its hide with its claws. But even this is rare.

The wanderlust hippo

On page 552 attention was drawn to the way crabeater seals have sometimes wandered well inland, for no obvious reason. Animals do this sort of thing occasionally, like the famous leopard of Mount Kilimanjaro, preserved in ice at 19 325 ft. Huberta was a famous hippopotamus that wandered a thousand miles. She left St Lucia Bay, in Zululand, in 1928 and wandered on and on until in 1931 she reached Cape Province. Each day she stopped to wallow in a river or lake, and her passage was noted in the local

newspapers all along her route, so her journey is fully documented. Throughout that time she never came into contact with another hippo. Huberta became almost a pet of the people of South Africa and a law was passed to protect her. She was finally shot, however, by a trigger-happy person in April 1931, and was then found to be a male. That lamentable bullet robbed the world of knowing how much farther Hubert might have wandered.

class	**Mammalia**
order	**Artiodactyla**
family	**Hippopotamidae**
genera & species	***Hippopotamus amphibius*** ***Choeropsis liberiensis*** *pygmy hippo*

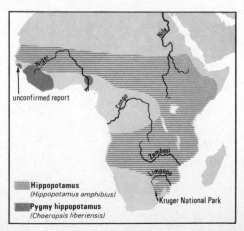

Hoatzin

Apparently a link with birds that became extinct millions of years ago, the hoatzin is one of the strangest of all living birds. It is classified with the domestic chicken in the order Galliformes but it is unique in many ways, being very primitive in some respects and very advanced in others. It is the size of a rook and looks rather like a scruffy pheasant with large wings and long, broad tail. The small head is set on a long thin neck, rather like a peacock's, except that instead of the peacock's gleaming feathers and immaculate crest there is a long crest of bristly feathers. Plumage on the upperparts is brown or bottle-green, streaked with white, and the underparts are white.

Restricted food supply

The hoatzin is restricted to flooded forests along big rivers in northern South America, from Guyana and Brazil to Bolivia and Colombia. These are the only places where the two plants on which the hoatzin feeds can be found. The diet of the hoatzin is almost entirely the leaves, flowers and fruit of the giant caladium and the pimpler thorn tree together with a few other marsh plants and occasional small crabs and fish. Most birds with such a restricted diet and habitat are usually threatened with extinction nowadays, but the hoatzin seems fairly

A Root: Photo Res

△ *A tree-clambering hoatzin youngster uses its wing-claws to good advantage.*

secure, at least for the moment, as the flooded forests of South America are relatively undisturbed and hoatzins are said to be unfit to eat, although their eggs are taken. They have a variety of local names, including 'Stinking Ana', that refers to the smell of hoatzin flesh. Apparently the unpleasantness is restricted to a musky odour which does not affect the taste of the flesh but is enough to put one off eating it.

Top-heavy bird

The hoatzin has a most peculiar digestive system which affects its whole life. In most plant-eating birds the food is first stored in the crop then ground up in a muscular gizzard. The hoatzin has a vestigial gizzard but the crop is much enlarged with thick walls and horny lining, both used to grind coarse leaves. The crop is high in the chest and a hoatzin tends to be top-heavy after a large meal. Its legs look strong but are not able to support it properly on its perch and hoatzins rest their bodies on the breastbone which is covered by a callosity: a pad of horny skin.

Another result of the strange digestive system is the hoatzin's weak power of flight. The huge crop takes up a large amount of room in the chest, at the expense of the flight muscles. The result is that the hoatzin can flap only feebly for short distances, perhaps 20 yd or so. Sometimes they climb to the tops of trees to flutter across a stream or pool. This is no great disadvantage as they live in dense forests with a ready supply of food in the form of lush vegetation.

▽ *Fossil of **Archaeopteryx,** the semi-reptilian earliest known bird, shows a common link with the young hoatzin: the wing claw (top centre). **Archaeopteryx,** too, was probably a poor flier.*

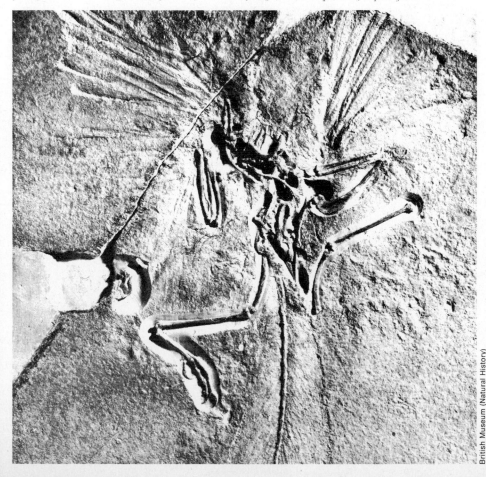

British Museum (Natural History)

1047

Hoatzins live in small flocks of 10—20 which stay together all the year round, as they often nest in colonies. The nests are rough platforms of twigs like pigeons' nests, about a dozen feet above the water. This is by no means a safe height as the rivers are liable to severe flooding. Both sexes build the nest and 2—4 small yellowish eggs are laid, but nothing is known about courtship or incubation. The noisy call, uttered with wings and tail spread, may play a part in courtship. The name hoatzin is said to be of Aztec origin and describing the bird's call.

The young hoatzins are the second of the truly remarkable features of this bird. When they hatch they are covered with the first of two coats of down. They spend a considerable time in the nest being fed by the parents in the manner of an Adélie penguin (p 15). The adult opens its mouth and the chick puts its bill in to take the food. Later the young leave the nest and crawl around the neighbouring branches. Each wing is equipped with two claws which the chicks use, with the bill, as an aid to clambering. They climb about with great agility and can evade capture this way. As a last resort they will leap off the branch and fall into the water. Here they continue to evade capture by repeated diving. When danger is past they climb back up to the nest. This behaviour is reminiscent of young darters (p 613) but darters are aquatic birds, and for a non-aquatic bird to use water to such an extent is quite remarkable.

Primitive wing-claws

The wing of a normal bird is built on the same pattern as the arms and legs of amphibians, reptiles and mammals: the pentadactyl or 5-fingered limb. In the wing the fourth and fifth fingers have been lost, the second and third bear the flight feathers and the 'thumb' forms the small 'bastard wing'. Fossils of *Archaeopteryx* show that this prehistoric bird had claws on the tips of each digit. It had feathers but the wings were so weak that it could not have flown properly and must have lived the same kind of life as the hoatzin, clambering around trees and gliding from one to another.

The hoatzin's chicks are so remarkable because they are even more like *Archaeopteryx*. They have two claws on each wing which can be moved by special muscles. The development of their wing feathers is retarded so the claws are free for hanging onto twigs and branches and the young hoatzins climb around on all fours. As they grow up the claws are lost and the wing feathers grow, but even as adults they still use their wings as aids to climbing. So, in following the growth of a hoatzin chick we are witnessing a very rapid demonstration of the evolution of birds, from a lizard-like creature climbing in the trees to a winged bird that can fly from one to another.

class	**Aves**
order	**Galliformes**
family	**Opisthocomidae**
genus & species	***Opisthocomus hoazin***

Constance P Warner

Hoatzin *(Opisthocomus hoazin)*

When seen from the front, the hoatzin's bristly crest and colourful head look rather like a peacock's — but there the resemblance ends abruptly. The hoatzin's long, drooping wings — large in relation to the body — have very weak flight muscles and sag below the body as a result. Young hoatzins have wing claws, with special muscles to move them, and in addition the development of their flight feathers is retarded. Although mature hoatzins lose their wing claws and their flight feathers develop normally, they still use their wings to clamber about in the dense foliage of their Amazon habitat (left). In doing this, they will often break their primary feathers.

Hobbies at the nest. The youngsters (at left) are rapidly shedding the white down which insulated them as chicks.

Hobby

The hobby is a small falcon, about 13 in. long. It has long scythe-like wings, narrower than those of a peregrine, and a comparatively short tail, giving it a swift-like silhouette. When perching the wings extend slightly beyond the tail. The upperparts are a slaty-brown and white underneath with conspicuous black stripes. There is a broad black stripe like a drooping moustache and the feathers forming 'leggings' covering the thighs are rusty red.

The hobby is rare in the British Isles, breeding only in the south of England where there are 75—100 pairs, mostly in Hampshire and neighbouring counties. It is widespread in the rest of Europe except in northern Scandinavia, Sicily, Sardinia and other Mediterranean islands. Hobbies are also found in northwest Africa and throughout temperate Asia to Kamchatka and the Kuriles. The African hobby is slightly smaller, 9½—11 in. compared to 12—14 in. long. It is found in eastern Africa from South Africa north to Ethiopia and across to Liberia.

The hobby is a summer resident in Europe, migrating to Africa in winter where it can be distinguished from its African counterpart by a generally paler plumage. In their breeding haunts in Europe, hobbies live in open woodland, on heath and downs with scattered clumps of trees or farmland with hedgerows, but in their winter home they prefer open savannah country.

It is rather difficult to tell whether hobbies have suffered from pesticides in recent years as they are most elusive birds during the breeding season and even in their narrow range in England it is difficult to make an accurate census. In 1931 Nethersole Thompson organised a search for hobbies and by combing several counties was able to find several new breeding places.

Fighter-ace predators

Hobbies hunt prey on the wing rather than pouncing on earth-bound prey, like harriers or kestrels. They stoop after small birds with great speed and agility, rivalling peregrines and merlins in aerial chases. They will also dash through flocks of swallows or starlings at breakneck speed, seizing one without checking or chasing a selected individual. Skylarks, martins and swallows are favoured prey but hobbies are known to take birds from the size of blue tits to the occasional pigeon or partridge.

Apart from birds, hobbies take many insects which do, in fact, form the bulk of their diet. They are hunted leisurely if slow fliers like beetles, or chased agilely if faster, like dragonflies, and are eaten in the air. In Africa hobbies prey on flying termites. They also prey on a few small mammals such as shrews and mice and occasionally take bats. On rare occasions hobbies have been seen to steal prey from kestrels.

Aerobatic antics

The aerial courtship of hobbies is even more spectacular than that of other birds of prey such as harriers (p 1027). A strident 'kew-kew-kew' often calls attention to a pair of hobbies as they prepare to indulge in their display of aerobatics. The pair will soar together, circling upwards until amost lost to sight and swoop at each other, circling around or looping the loop and occasionally flapping over to glide upside down. The culmination of these displays of aerobatic skill comes when the male brings food to the female. Male harriers pass food to the female in flight, but the male hobby does so at higher speeds. He dives at full speed from a great height then soars up as he passes the female, and she takes the prey from him.

Like other falcons, hobbies do not build their own nests but take over the deserted nests of other species, often flattening them and removing part of the original lining. Nests of carrion crows and other members of the crow family are most often used, together with those of herons, wood pigeons, sparrowhawks and squirrels. The normal clutch consists of three eggs which are incubated mainly by the female. Like the female harrier, she is called off the nest by the male to be given food either at a nearby perch or in the air. After the chicks have hatched she may collect food for them in this manner or the male will land at the nest. The female begins to bring food when the chicks are quite large, unless the pair are feeding mainly on insects. Then both hobbies hunt, bringing small amounts of food at short intervals. The young fly when one month old and for a short time are fed in the air by the parents.

Nimble killers

Only in recent years have patterns of hunting and escape behaviour been studied in detail. Lions and other cats stalk their prey then bound out at them, giving up quickly if the quarry eludes them. Dogs like the Cape hunting dog tirelessly run down their prey, sometimes chasing it for miles. The reaction of many animals to an attack is not to run away as fast as possible, which seems the obvious thing to do, but to jink about trying to outwit and out-manoeuvre the enemy. This is especially useful against the dash-and-give-up type of predator like cats, but some hunting animals have become particularly adept at following their prey's erratic movements. One such animal is the bat-eared fox (p 163) that can follow gerbils as they double back on their tracks. Hobbies also have this ability. In falconry they were used to hunt larks, that attempt to escape by complicated manoeuvres, and incredible aerial 'dogfights' can be seen between hobbies and swallows or swifts, and even dragonflies which flash back and forth as if on a spring. Once a hobby was seen to swoop underneath a swallow and, flipping over, sink its talons into the swallow's belly.

class	**Aves**
order	**Falconiformes**
family	**Falconidae**
genus & species	*Falco cuvieri* African hobby *F. subbuteo* hobby

Hochstetter's frog is a New Zealander, living near mountain tops where the air is always moist and cool. It is small—never growing larger than 2 in.—and its toes are only partly webbed.

Hochstetter's frog

Hochstetter's frog is here chosen as a representative of the primitive frog family Leiopelmidae of which three species live in New Zealand, with the only other species in northwest America—the opposite corner of the Pacific. Although none of the four species has a tail they still have two tail-wagging muscles. The toes are only slightly webbed. Each vertebra is concave on both faces, a condition known as amphicoelous. The vertebrae of nearly all fishes are amphicoelous, those of all other frogs are not. Hochstetter's frog and its relatives seem therefore to be very near the early fish-like ancestors of amphibians and it is tempting to think that they have found sanctuary in mountains, as described for hillstream fishes. The Leiopelmidae are not only the most primitive frogs, but are very rare. They are protected in New Zealand.

Tailed froglets . . .

Hochstetter's frog and its relatives are less than 2 in. long. They live mainly near mountain tops where the air is moist and cold and the temperature of any water there may be is usually not above 4°C/40°F. They are chiefly interesting for the way they breed. The eggs of Hochstetter's frog were found in November and December of 1949 in the seepage from a mountain stream, in tunnels in the wet clay. The tunnels were probably made by dragonfly larvae. On the floors of the tunnels the eggs, $\frac{3}{16}$ in. diameter when laid and strung together like beads in groups of 2—8, lie on the mud washed by slow trickles of water. Near the mouths of the tunnels the males sit as if guarding the eggs. There is no tadpole; the embryo develops and grows through the tadpole stages within the egg. All the fluid necessary for development is inside the eggs. The first froglets appear 41 days after being laid but not all eggs in one clutch hatch at the same time. Those in large clusters take several days to hatch, some being as much as 9 days after the first hatch. For the first month after hatching the froglet lives on the remains of yolk from the egg. It breaks out of the egg by lashing with its long tail, and this then becomes an important breathing organ. The lungs do not develop fully for some weeks after hatching, and in the meantime the froglet breathes through the skin of the belly and tail, both of which are richly supplied with fine surface blood vessels.

Archey's frog, also on the New Zealand mountains, lays its eggs under stones, but otherwise behaves like Hochstetter's frog. Its food is insects and larvae, spiders and woodlice or sowbugs. These frogs have a large tongue, rounded or pearshaped, almost completely fastened to the floor of the mouth, so it cannot be shot out to capture prey.

. . . and tailed frogs

The American relative has been variously called tailed frog and American bell toad.

It lives in the Rockies from southern British Columbia through Washington to Oregon, on the western side, and in Idaho and western Montana, on the eastern side. It lives in the swift, icy mountain streams and at breeding time from May to September the males, which are voiceless, creep about the bed of the stream to find the females. The females lay their eggs in strings of 30—50 fastened to the undersides of rocks. The eggs hatch a month later and within an hour the black or blackish tadpoles, up to 2 in. long, grow a triangular adhesive disc on the head. Using this they cling to rocks, so avoiding being swept away by the current. They often use it to climb above water onto the wet rock, and during rain will travel overland for distances of up to 100 ft.

The tadpole is peculiar in having funnel-like nostrils that it can close when the rush of water is too great. They can also be closed to regulate the flow of water through the mouth and across the gills for breathing. The tadpoles scrape small algae from the rocks for food while holding on with the sucker, and turn into froglets the following year, between July and September.

Tailed frogs are so completely adapted to low temperatures that if trees around their home are felled, so more sunlight gets through to raise the temperature of the water, they move into more sheltered spots. The name has nothing to do with the way the froglet retains its tail longer than is usual in the commoner frogs. It is from an apparent tail seen in the male. This is an extension of the cloaca which is used in mating, to give internal fertilization. External fertilization, more usual in frogs, would be impossible in the fast-flowing streams, as the sperm would be washed away. This organ looks slightly like a tail and presumably has given rise to the name.

No voice, no ears?

The males of typical frogs croak and all frogs have ears, apart from Hochstetter's frog and its relatives. They have what appear to be degenerate ears. They lack both eardrum and Eustachian tube (the tube that connects the inner ear with the throat). It has been suggested that tailed frogs are voiceless and at least semi-deaf because of the turbulent streams in which they live. Presumably the reasoning is like this. The females would not hear the males calling because of the noise made by the gushing, tinkling mountain streams. So males have lost their voices because they are useless. Since the frogs are voiceless, there is no use for ears, and these have degenerated. Those who propounded this theory cannot be aware of the 'cocktail party' effect, when the ear ignores the heavy babble and chatter all around and picks out one particular voice or sound.

class	**Amphibia**		
order	**Salientia**		
family	**Leiopelmidae**		
genera & species	***Ascaphus truei*** *American tailed frog*		
	Leiopelma archeyi *Archey's frog*		
	L. hochstetteri *Hochstetter's frog*		
	L. hamiltoni *Hamilton's frog*		

Hog-nosed snake

The three species of hog-nosed snakes are named after the sharply upturned tip of their snouts, like those of farmyard hogs. The head is short and broad, the tail short and the body thick. The colour is very variable, commonly olive green, brownish, grey or slate. There is usually a row of dark bars or blotches and a row of spots along either side. In darker animals the blotches and spots are obscured. The underside is yellowish or whitish mottled with brown or grey. The overall colour of individual hog-nosed snakes depends on their habitat. Those living in woodland are generally darker than those living in dry sandy places.

The eastern hog-nosed snake is the largest species, usually 18—30 in. long, with a record of 48 in. It is found from Ontario in Canada to Florida and Texas. The western hog-nosed snake (shown here) is usually 16—21 in. long, and lives on sandy prairies from Alberta to Central Mexico. In southeastern United States there is the southern hog-nosed snake, the smallest of them all at 12—27 in. long.

Eastern hog-nosed snake, largest of the three species, shams dead in the picture below.

ing adder', 'puff adder' and 'hissing sand snake', and it has also led to the hog-nosed snake being killed on sight.

If this impressive display of ferocity fails to send an enemy fleeing, the hog-nosed snake abruptly changes its tactics and rolls over, limp, with mouth open and tongue hanging out, even giving a realistic final death twitch. Like the grass snake that has the same trick, the hog-nosed snake will persist in rolling onto its back whenever it is turned onto its belly.

Yet another bluff?

Hog-nosed snakes may have been double-crossing people all along. It is firmly stated that they are not venomous, one writer even saying that they cannot have poison glands because they are not poisonous! Yet a person's hand has been known to swell up and become painful after a bite from a hog-nosed snake. The long teeth in the back of

▽ *Hog-nosed snakes are found in nearly every state in the eastern half of North America, from Canada to the Gulf of Mexico.*

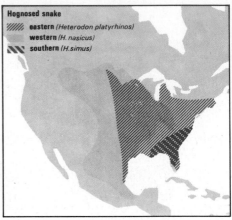

Hognosed snake
///// **eastern** (*Heterodon platyrhinos*)
western (*H. nasicus*)
\\\\ **southern** (*H.simus*)

Eating frogs and toads

The hog-nosed snake's snout is apparently used as a shovel when the snake burrows through loose soil. It prefers dry, sandy country in the prairie districts of North America, but it can also be found in orchards and swamps. As far as is known its prey consists largely of frogs and toads—mainly the latter—but as it burrows through the soil it would be surprising if young snakes did not take worms and other soil-dwelling animals. It has been known to eat small mammals, birds, lizards and snakes. Prey is seized and swallowed head first, assisted by long fang-like teeth in the back of the mouth. It has been suggested that the snakes use these teeth to puncture the skins of toads that have inflated themselves in self-defence. In Michigan, however, observations showed that hog-nosed snakes fed entirely on toads, and where the toads' habitat was being destroyed by drainage and building the snakes were becoming rare.

Eggs swell before hatching

Eggs are laid in a damp place, such as under a rotting log, in June or July. Each female lays 12—30 white, leathery eggs, occasionally more. As they develop, the eggs swell and, just before hatching, they are nearly spherical and have increased in volume by one-third. Newly-hatched eastern hognosed snakes measure 6—8 in. and are grey rather than brownish like the parents, but they have the rows of dark markings.

Two-line defence

Hog-nosed snakes belong to the family Colubridae. Most of the snakes in this family are harmless but some of them have developed means of deterring enemies. The grass snake (p 934) feigns death and the egg-eating snake (p 692) mimics poisonous snakes or pretends to be dangerous by inflating the front part of its body, coiling up, hissing and even striking. This is enough to convince most enemies that it is well to keep clear, especially as the egg-eating snake resembles venomous vipers. The false coral snakes (p 526) of a different family also mimic poisonous snakes. The hog-nosed snakes too are impostors with a variety of acts. Some of them resemble the poisonous massasanga rattlesnake. Moreover, if disturbed, they show off the markings on the skin by inflating the front half of the body and neck by spreading their ribs and adjusting the jaw bones until there is a hood like that of an angry cobra (p 463). In all of them the next step is to hiss and strike at their adversary, but with the mouth shut. This behaviour has led to such names as 'spread-

its mouth do not have grooves down which poison could flow, as in poisonous members of the Colubridae, but the secretions from their parotid glands, the modified salivary glands, which in snakes produce venom, could still be toxic and their poison be painful if it got into an open wound. Some species of oriental grass snakes have poisonous salivary glands. In considering 'borderline' cases like this, it must be remembered that animals are still evolving; in a million years from now, several of the 'harmless' snakes could well have an efficient venom apparatus.

class	**Reptilia**
order	**Squamata**
suborder	**Serpentes**
family	**Colubridae**
genus & species	*Heterodon nasicus* western hog-nosed snake
	H. platyrhinos eastern hog-nosed snake
	H. simus southern hog-nosed snake

Honey ant

Also called honey-pot ants, these are species living in dry or desert regions, in which some of the workers remain in the nest and act as living storage vessels. They are then known as 'repletes'. The habit has been developed independently in various groups of ants belonging to two subfamilies, the Camponotinae and Dolichoderinae, living in North America, Australia and Africa. The so-called 'honey' is a sugary solution obtained by the ants from aphids and, in America, from the secretion of a gall growing on small oak trees. The habit is developed in deserts because this source of food is not available during long periods of drought.

*A kind of half-way condition is seen in the common American ant **Prenolepis imparis**. It feeds largely on honeydew from aphids, and the workers have unusually distensible abdomens which are often seen swollen to a 'semi-replete' condition. This probably represents a stage in the evolution of the fully developed honey ants.*

More take than give

In the nest of the honey ants some of the workers fail to go out foraging with the rest, and remain at home from the time they leave the pupa. They are perfectly normal ants, at first differing in no way from the workers which hunt for food and perform ordinary duties in the nest. But their behaviour is peculiar. Ants constantly feed each other, mouth to mouth, and these individuals accept food from incoming workers far beyond their own needs. They also give food to others when it is solicited, but on balance, when plenty is available, they take far more than they give.

As a consequence of this excessive intake the abdomen of these ants becomes more and more distended, taking the form of a globe $\frac{1}{4}-\frac{1}{3}$ in. diameter. It is translucent with narrow black bars, which are the body segments that were in contact with each other when the ant had its normal shape. When fully replete they hang from the roof of the deeper chambers of the nest. If one of them falls it cannot move, as its fantastically swollen stomach is far too heavy, even if it happens to land in a position from which its feet can reach the ground. If its overloaded crop splits and spills its burden, the other workers rush to enjoy the feast, wholly disregarding the fate of their crippled sister.

Dies to feed others

While there is green vegetation around and food is plentiful the hanging repletes are constantly visited by incoming ants and persuaded to add more and more to their store. In time of drought, when the foragers return empty or cease trying to find food in the parched and sterile desert, visitors to the repletes solicit the mixed food and water, and their swollen bellies gradually diminish. They can never return to a normal existence, however, as the stretched skin of their abdomens cannot contract. They probably die as soon as their store is exhausted.

When supplies are coming in and all the established repletes are distended to capacity, any young worker ant may accept a proffered drop from an incoming worker and then find herself besieged by more and more of them until she begins to swell and climbs for comfort to the roof of the chamber. Her fate is then sealed; instead of taking her place as an active, busy member of the community, she must spend the rest of her life as an inert, swollen barrel of syrup.

Honey ants were first discovered in 1881 by an American cleric named Henry C McCook. The scene of their discovery was the Garden of the Gods in Colorado, and the classically minded McCook gave the ant the specific name *horti-deorum*, Latin for the romantically sounding name of its home territory. It is now regarded as a subspecies of *Myrmecocystus mexicanus*.

Ants on the menu

The country people of Mexico search eagerly for the nests of these ants and regard the swollen repletes as a gastronomic delicacy. It is not easy work digging them out as the ants nest on dry ridges where the soil is very hard; but the reward is worth the effort since a well-stocked nest may contain 50 repletes and sometimes as many as 300 may be found. The American entomologist Dr Alexander Klots writes of the repletes, massed along the ceiling of a horizontal gallery, as gleaming like amber beads in the rays of a flashlight. He describes their contents as 'extremely sweet and delicately flavoured, far surpassing, in our opinion, honeybee honey'. The Australian Aborigines living in the Central Desert also dig out the honey ants and the smiles on their faces, showing their flashing white teeth, are eloquent testimony to the tastiness of the honey ants. They hold the ant's thorax between thumb and forefinger and nip off the honey-filled abdomen with their teeth.

Walker Van Riper

Bulging honey ant repletes gleam like amber beads, their abdomen plates grotesquely separated.

Graham Pizzey

phylum	**Arthropoda**
class	**Insecta**
order	**Hymenoptera**
family	**Formicidae**
sub-families	**Camponotinae and Dolichoderinae**
genera	***Myrmecocystus** (America); **Plagiolepis** (Africa); **Melophorus, Leptomyrmex, Camponotus** (Australia)*

Honey badger enjoys a stretch and a yawn. Its powerful wicked-looking claws can tackle all-comers.

Honey badger

Closely related to the Old World and American badgers, the honey badger resembles them in build, being short-legged with a heavy body and short tail. The legs are extremely powerful and the forefeet bear claws longer and stouter than those of an Old World badger. The head and body of a honey badger total $2-2\frac{1}{2}$ ft long with a tail of $8-10$ in. and it stands about 1 ft high at the shoulder. The underparts and sides of the body are dark brown or black, while the top of the head, neck and back are grey or whitish — the reverse of the usual animal coloration and making the honey badger particularly conspicuous in daylight. Some honey badgers, especially in the Ituri forest of the Congo, are wholly black. Several of the family Mustelidae have striking black and white patterns, including polecats, skunks, weasels and badgers. In some cases at least it seems that this is warning coloration, telling predators that such animals are best left alone. The skunk, with its habit of squirting a powerful and irritating liquid at its enemies, is a good example. The colours of the honey badger appear to serve the same purpose: it is an aggressive animal and can secrete an evil-smelling fluid from its tail glands.

Honey badgers are found in most of Africa from Senegal and the Sudan to the Cape Province. They also range across Asia from Arabia and Turkestan to India. They are nowhere common and are becoming rarer in the face of advancing human settlement.

Nocturnal prowlers

Honey badgers live in many kinds of country, including rocky hills, forests, savannah and waterless plains, but although well-spread, they are not often seen because of their nocturnal habits. During the day honey badgers lie up under rocks or in abandoned aardvark holes, and if these are not available they will dig their own burrows. Occasionally, however, they may be seen out on dull, cloudy days. They roam about singly or in pairs, except when the cubs are taken out by their parents.

A formidable foe

Almost any kind of food is acceptable to honey badgers. They eat fruits and berries and all sorts of animals, especially insects. Tortoises are eaten after their shells have been smashed by the honey badgers' strong teeth and quite large snakes are tackled. A ranger in the Kruger National Park once came upon a honey badger attacking a $10-11$ ft python. Stones and dust were flying in all directions but eventually the python succumbed, looking as if it had been run over by a train. Their thick skin makes honey badgers almost immune to venomous snakes such as cobras which they also catch. Honey badgers often dig up the burrows of ground squirrels, suricates, rats and mice and eat the occupants and they will attack porcupines, being protected from their quills by their tough skin. Sometimes honey badgers are hunted because they kill livestock such as sheep and chickens.

Honey badgers have developed a remarkable association with a bird called a honeyguide. In tropical Africa this bird attracts the attention of honey badgers, man and perhaps other animals with a special call and leads them to a bees' nest. The honey badger or man then breaks open the nest for the honey, while the honeyguide feeds on the wax of the combs that are scattered about. Once again, the honey badger's tough skin saves it, this time from the angry bees. The relationship between the honeyguide and its followers is discussed on page 1097.

Keeping its breeding secrets

Very little has been recorded about the breeding habits of the honey badger. Most activities take place at night and its ferocious disposition must discourage close investigation. The young, usually two per litter, are reared in burrows or in deep crevices in rocks. The gestation is apparently 6 months.

Running amok

Honey badgers must be the most ferocious animals for their size if not the most ferocious of all animals. They seem to be incapable of fear and will sometimes attack without provocation, especially during the breeding season when they will charge from their burrows. Horses and cattle are sometimes attacked like this and there is even a record of a Cape buffalo, whose own dangerous reputation is discussed on page 360, being knocked down and killed. Despite this the honey badger is said to make a very good pet if caught before it is half grown, although some owners tell of their fits of tantrums when such pets had to be left alone. It would seem, however, that their boisterous playful nature and habit of marking objects with musk would make them generally unacceptable as pets.

The honey badger's success as a fighter is not just a result of its long claws and strong teeth. Any enemy that can get past these weapons finds a honey badger difficult to kill. Its skin, impervious to bee sting and snake bite, is exceptionally tough and has been described as being 'like a loose coating of rubber'. If an opponent grabs it by the scruff of its neck the honey badger can turn round inside its skin and deliver a severe bite. There are records of honey badgers engaging a pack of dogs and, after a fight of bear-baiting proportions, trotting away leaving the dogs exhausted and wounded.

class	**Mammalia**
order	**Carnivora**
family	**Mustelidae**
genus & species	*Mellivora capensis*

Honeybee

*Any of the four species of social bees belonging to the genus **Apis** can be called honeybees but the name is most usually associated with the European domestic bee **Apis mellifera**, sometimes called the western honeybee. This differs from all other social bees and social wasps of temperate climates in forming colonies that survive the winter by living on reserve stores of food, so a particular dwelling site or nest may be occupied for an indefinite length of time. In social wasps and bumble bees all the members of the colony die at the end of the summer except the fertilised females or queens, which hibernate and found new colonies in the following spring.*

In the colonies of social bees, wasps and ants there are two kinds of females. The fertile females are called 'queens' and the sterile females are the 'workers', the latter doing all the work of maintaining the economy of the colony. In the wasps, most bees and some ants the egg-laying organ or ovipositor of both types of female is transformed to a sting, connected with a poison gland. In the queens the eggs are extruded from an opening at the base of the sting.

Bees have been kept for their honey by man for many hundreds of years. Throughout most of history this has been mainly a matter of inducing them to make colonies in hollow receptacles of various kinds, such as earthenware pots, logs and straw baskets or 'skeps', and then robbing them of their honey. Until recently their breeding has been entirely uncontrolled and even now they are not domesticated in the same way as dogs, cattle, or even silkworms.

Household chores

The great majority of European honeybees are now living in hives although wild colonies may be found, almost always in hollow trees. In midsummer a strong colony normally contains one queen, 50 000 to 60 000 workers and a few hundred males or drones. The expectation of life of a worker bee at this time is only 4–6 weeks and her span is divided into two periods. For just under 3 weeks after emerging from the pupa the worker's duties lie within the hive, where she is fed at first by older bees, but later feeds herself from the stores of honey and pollen. Her first spell of work is as nursemaid to the developing larvae, to whom she passes on a great deal of the food she eats, partly by direct regurgitation and partly by giving them a jelly-like secretion from certain salivary glands in her head. By the time she is about 12 days old her wax glands have developed and she turns to building and repairing the comb of geometrically arranged cells in which the larvae are reared and food is stored. At this time she also goes out for short flights around the hive, learning the landmarks by which to guide herself home when she ventures farther afield.

Pollination in action; this vital link between animal and plant life is demonstrated here by a honeybee worker and a Jupiter's distaff **(Salvia glutinosa)**. *The bee drones in towards the plant's gaping mouth, lands on the 'lower lip' section of the corolla, and sets to work collecting the plant's nectar. Triggered by the bee's activity, the plant's pollen-bearing anther extends outwards and downwards, brushing its covering of pollen onto the bee's back to be carried on to the next flower the bee visits.*

Series by Herman Eisenbeiss

From about 12 days to 3 weeks old she takes over the nectar and pollen brought in by returning foragers, converting the former to honey and storing it away. At the same time she helps to keep the hive tidy, carrying outside dead bees and other debris. At 3 weeks old she is ready to go out foraging herself for nectar, pollen, water and resin, which are the four substances needed for the hive's economy. The last is used to make a sort of varnish-like cement called 'propolis' with which crevices and any small openings in the hive are sealed up.

Searching for nectar

In searching for nectar-yielding flowers the worker bee is guided by her senses of smell and sight. Bees have good colour vision but it differs from our own. They cannot see red at all but can see ultraviolet 'colour', invisible to us but revealed by photography by ultraviolet light. Bees guide themselves to and from the hive by reference to the angle of the sun, or of polarised light from the sky, and have a time sense which enables them to compensate for the continuous change in the sun's position.

Foraging is very hard work and after 2–3 weeks of it the worker is worn out and dies. Workers hatched in the autumn have a much longer life before them, as they build up food reserves in their bodies and their activity is reduced through the winter. They keep warm by huddling together in a mass and feeding on the honey that they have stored.

The queen rules her great horde of daughters, not by example or wise counsel, but by secreting from her body a substance whose presence or absence controls their behaviour. Her chief role, however, is egg-laying, and at midsummer she may be laying 1 500 eggs a day, totalling more than the weight of her own body. This enormous fecundity is needed to compensate for the shortness of the workers' lives.

The idle drones

Mating with and fertilising the queens is the only useful part played in honeybee economy by the drones. During summer they usually live 4–5 weeks and are fed by the workers, not even seeking their own food among the flowers. In autumn the drones remaining in the colony are turned outside to die of starvation or chill.

New colonies are founded by what is known as swarming. As a preliminary to this extra queens are produced in the hive and then large numbers of workers, accompanied by some drones and usually one queen, leave the hive and fly together for some distance. Then they settle in a large cluster and search for a suitable place, where a new colony is made by some of the workers. At this stage they can easily be persuaded to settle down in artificial quarters of any kind merely by shaking the swarm, with its attendant queen, into a suitable receptacle, such as a beehive.

Natural and artificial breeding

Queens may be produced in a hive in response to ageing of the mother queen or to the urge to swarm. In either case they fly out to seek mates when they are about a week old. A drone that mates with a queen

Searching for new homes; western honeybees settle in a large cluster on an apple tree and scouts search for a new home. The swarm is made up of large numbers of workers, a few drones, and an extra queen who was produced in the formerly overcrowded hive. While settled they can be persuaded to take to artificial quarters of any kind merely by shaking the swarm, with its attendant queen, into a suitable container—straw 'skep' or wooden hive. The next stage is an egg-laying marathon.

The swarm is installed in its new home. After her nuptial flight, the queen gets down to the tedious job of laying 1 500 eggs a day, each one deposited in a carefully-constructed hexagonal cell forming a unit in the wax comb.

S Dalton: NHPA

John Markham

Colin G Butler

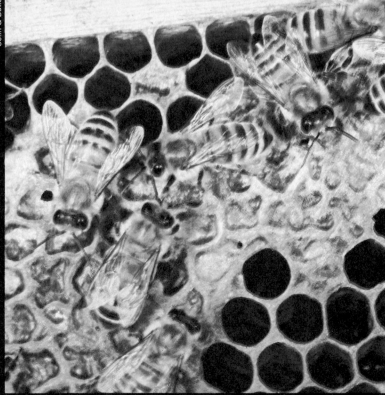

Colin G Butler

A drone makes landfall beside the queen, who is surrounded by workers. From her body the queen secretes a substance whose presence or absence controls the behaviour of the great horde of her daughter-workers, who shoulder the death-dealing burden of supplying the hive or colony. To do this, the workers have developed an efficient communications system.

Method in their madness: this is a workers' conference, carried out in dance language. To tell each other where flower-nectar is to be found, bee workers have evolved two sorts of dance: a round dance for nearby nectar and a tail-wagging dance for distant nectar. They perform both of these subtle evolutions on the vertical face of the honeycomb.

Royal birth: a queen struggles out of her cell. The larvae are fed partly on a mixture of honey and pollen and partly on a secretion from various glands of the young worker bee. This is the substance often referred to as 'royal jelly'.

Workers' feeding-time on sugar solution. They are born from fertile eggs laid in a normal cell; the resulting larvae are fed first on 'royal jelly' and later on pollen and honey. But when a queen is produced, the workers make larger cells into which the reigning queen lays ordinary fertilised eggs. The larvae from these eggs are fed only on 'royal jelly' until they become fully-developed queens, ready to hatch. Drone larvae are fed like workers, but take 8 days to develop instead of 6 days.

Friedel Schöx

S Dalton: NHPA

Heinz Schrempp

André Fatras

Man collects the spoils, prudently protected by anti-sting veils and smoke-tins. Bees have been kept by man for their honey for many centuries. The history of bee-keeping has mainly been a matter of inducing the bees to make colonies in various kinds of hollow receptacle, such as earthenware pots or straw baskets, then plundering the honey.

A sight to gladden the heart of Pooh Bear — or any bear if it comes to that — a tree-suspended nest of wild bees. These are fairly innocuous in the West, but the huge wild bees of the Orient are extremely dangerous if too many liberties are taken with their nests, and infuriated swarms of them have caused several deaths among unwary human prowlers.

condemns himself to death. The reason for this is that his genital organs become so firmly fixed in the queen's body that they are torn out when the two bees part, and he dies almost immediately. The sperm is stored by the queen in an internal sac called the spermatheca, and sperms are released to fertilise the eggs as she lays them. Here there is a strange departure from the condition normally found in animals. All eggs that are fertilised produce females, either workers or queens; drones are only produced from eggs that develop without being fertilised.

The larva and pupa stages of honeybees (collectively known as the 'brood') are passed in the wax cells into which the eggs are laid, one in each cell. The larvae are entirely helpless and are fed by the workers. The

flowers; nectar and honey are chemically distinct and the latter is much more concentrated. The larvae are fed partly on a mixture of nectar or honey and pollen and partly on a secretion from various glands of the young workers, the substance that is often called 'royal jelly'. When a fertilised egg is laid in a normal sized cell the larva is fed at first on jelly and later on pollen and honey, and it develops into a worker. When production of queens is needed the workers make larger cells into which the reigning queen lays ordinary fertilised eggs. The larvae from these, however, are fed until they are fully grown on royal jelly alone and they develop into queens. Drone larvae are fed similarly to those of workers but for 2 more days, 8 instead of 6.

Bees will readily drink a solution of sugar

Fierce relatives

Only four species of the genus *Apis* are known, and one of them, the eastern honeybee *Apis indica*, is so similar to *Apis mellifera* it is sometimes regarded as a subspecies. It is domesticated in tropical Asia.

Both the other species inhabit the eastern tropics. The giant honeybee *Apis dorsata* is a large bee which makes enormous hanging combs in the open. An overhanging surface is chosen at a considerable height from the ground. Large branches overhanging cliffs and buildings, especially water towers, are favourite sites for colonies. These bees may be dangerous if molested and there are records of people being attacked and stung to death. Nevertheless the Dyaks of Borneo climb by night with smoking torches, throw

Friedel Schöx

1. Ouch! A bee sting lances into a finger. The sting has several small barbs near the end; when the bee tries to pull out the sting it often breaks from the bee's body, fatally injuring the bee.
2. Section through a queen's abdomen shows stored egg clusters.
3. A worker's honey stomach, where nectar is stored before being regurgitated on return to the hive.
4. Each bee leg does a different job:
a: Rear legs scrape pollen into the pollen baskets. b: Stiff hairs on the middle legs brush pollen from the thorax and front legs. c: Front legs have branched feathery hairs for collecting pollen. The special joint (arrowed) cleans both eyes and antennae.
5. Compound eye of bee provides colour vision.

Photos by Gene Cox

pollen basket

development of a worker bee takes 21 days, 3 as an egg, 6 as a larva and 12 as a pupa.

The natural mating behaviour of queen and drone bees makes any control of pairing and breeding impossible, but in recent years a technique for artificially inseminating chosen queens with sperm from chosen drones has been developed. It is a difficult process requiring delicate manipulation under a microscope, but by this means selected strains of bees can now be bred.

'Common' and 'royal' food

The natural food of bees consists of nectar and pollen, the nectar supplying the energy-producing sugar and the pollen being a source of protein. The bees also make honey from nectar and store it for food. It is untrue to say that bees suck honey from

in water and are often fed on this during the winter by bee keepers who take most of their stored honey but are also concerned to keep their bees alive.

Enemies and disease

In spite of their stings bees are preyed upon by birds, dragonflies and some kinds of wasps. Certain moths called wax moths lay their eggs in the hives and the larvae live on wax, pollen and general comb debris, doing serious damage if they are at all numerous. The big death's-head hawk moth is said to invade colonies and steal the honey, piercing the wax comb with its short, stiff proboscis. It was called the 'Bee Tyger' by the early entomologists.

The greatest menace to honeybees, however, is disease and starvation.

down the combs and gather the honey.

The little honeybee *Apis florea* is by contrast an inoffensive little insect, reluctant to use its sting. A colony consists of a single comb the size of the palm of a man's hand, which contains only 1 or 2 oz. of honey.

In tropical America stingless bees of the genus *Trigona* (not closely related to the Old World honeybees) make large colonies in hollow logs and similar places and they used to be domesticated for their honey by the Maya Indians of Mexico.

phylum	**Arthropoda**
class	**Insecta**
order	**Hymenoptera**
family	**Apidae**

Honey buzzard

Although they are hawks, honey buzzards are so named because they feed largely on bees and wasps and, in flight, have a silhouette very much like a buzzard. The wing feathers are splayed at the tips but the wings as a whole are longer and narrower, and the head and neck are longer than in buzzards. The upperparts are dark brown, and the underparts range from white with a few dark markings to a dark brown similar to the upperparts. The honey buzzard breeds in most of Europe and spreads as far east as Lake Balkash and the River Ob, but is missing from the greater part of Scandinavia. In the British Isles, the honey buzzard has never been common but still breeds in a few places, especially in the south.

The related crested honey buzzard lives in India, China, eastern Siberia, parts of Japan, southeast Asia and the surrounding islands. In the Celebes and Philippines there is the barred honey buzzard and the long-tailed honey buzzard lives in New Guinea and some neighbouring islands.

Crowded commuters

Honey buzzards live in woodland where there are large trees and are often found in clearings or along more open ground by the side of roads or streams. At the end of the breeding season the European honey buzzards migrate to central and southern Africa while those breeding farther east move south to India and southeast Asia. Migrating honey buzzards often travel in large numbers, not so much in flocks as in continuous streams following well-defined routes —along the banks of lakes, for example. They cross the Mediterranean at Gibraltar or other places where the sea crossing is as short as possible, swarming across when the weather is favourable. Many birds cross the Straits of Gibraltar or the Bosphorus on their way to Africa. The larger birds such as hawks or storks soar upwards in thermals over the land then glide across the sea using the minimum of energy. Unfortunately they are shot regularly and persistently as they migrate through southern Europe, which is unnecessary and even foolish, as honey buzzards rarely attack birds or mammals but prey mainly on wasps, which can be pests in orchards.

Concentrating on wasps

The honey buzzard is also known as the wasp buzzard and this is a better name as its main food is the grubs of wasps. It does occasionally eat honey and wax but the name of honey buzzard was probably given because it was often seen digging out the combs from the large nests of wasps and honeybees, as well as the smaller nests of bumble bees. The honey buzzard's main interest in the combs is the grubs and pupae.

Not surprisingly, the honey buzzard is not seen soaring high in the air as often as the common buzzard; its food is near or on the ground and honey buzzards can be seen running about very nimbly. Having detected

JC Chantelat

△ *Watchful parent, with fledglings that are just losing their last traces of white down.*

▽ *A highly-decorated nest! The first food of the chick consists of grubs from wasp's combs.*

JC Chantelat

a nest they dig it out, scraping earth back with both feet and pulling out pieces of comb. Sometimes quite a deep hole is necessary and honey buzzards have been seen disappearing into pits 16 in. deep.

Honey buzzards have been described as hardly worthy of being called birds of prey, because of their preference for digging out bee and wasp nests. They will, however, also feed on ants, moths, cockchafers and locusts and occasionally take small mammals, slugs, snakes, worms, frogs and eggs and nestlings of other birds. They also eat a little fruit.

ently with excitement, when the sprays are brought in, and then play with them.

The usual clutch is of 2 eggs which are incubated for about 5 weeks, mainly by the female. The chicks are fed at first on wasp grubs which are regurgitated to them, or else the male brings pieces of comb and the female picks out the grubs and hands them over to the chicks. Later frogs are brought and, until the chicks learn to deal with them, they are skinned by the parents. The chicks fly when 5–7 weeks old. It is difficult to estimate the exact time because, until they can balance on one leg properly and hold a

ever, is not the adult insects but the defenceless grubs which do not need treatment. The honey buzzards are, however, in danger of being stung by aggrieved worker wasps and bees. The plumage is no doubt sufficient protection and honey buzzards have special scale-like feathers around the eyes and base of the bill. One Danish ornithologist watched a honey buzzard for 10 hours from a hide while it dug up a wasps' nest. The buzzing throng of wasps seemed to annoy it and it repeatedly pecked at them, cutting their heads off. It did not bother to eat them, presumably preferring the grubs.

JC Chantelat

Decorating the nest

Courtship is like that of true buzzards, swooping and soaring as if on a switchback. At the top of the soar the honey buzzard hovers for a few seconds and claps its wings over its back two or three times in quick succession. Both birds also soar high over the nest and the male dives at the female.

The nest is usually built on the abandoned nest of a crow or buzzard in a tall tree, beech being preferred. Both sexes decorate the nest, bringing fresh sprigs of greenery each evening to line it. When the chicks have hatched they squeal, appar-

piece of comb in the foot, the chicks return to the nest to feed. They also return to the nest to roost every night.

Avoiding the sting

We have seen how bee-eaters (p 182) treat bees to remove their stings before eating them, so it is not surprising to find that honey buzzards do the same. No one seems to have studied their method of dealing with adult bees and wasps in detail although wasps found in their crops have had their abdomens bitten off. Their main food, how-

Booty holder: A honey buzzard grips a comb from which it will dig out the grubs and larvae.

class	**Aves**
order	**Falconiformes**
family	**Accipitridae**
genera & species	***Pernis apivorus*** *honey buzzard* ***P. ptilorhynchus*** *crested honey buzzard* ***P. celebensis*** *barred honey buzzard* ***Henicopernis longicauda*** *long-tailed honey buzzard*

Marital strife: a pair of honeycreepers—black-faced dacnis **Dacnis lineata** *—display at each other.*

Honeycreeper

There are two groups of birds called honey-creepers. One group consists of birds related to tanagers and wood-warblers that have developed the habit of nectar eating. The other group is the Hawaiian honeycreepers, birds that invaded the islands of Hawaii and developed a variety of forms, like Darwin's finches in the Galapagos Islands.

Many of the first group are known as sugarbirds, especially to bird fanciers, which is confusing because some of the honeyeaters (see next entry) also have this name. They are small with thin bills and the males are usually brilliantly coloured, often with beautiful shades of blue. The females are duller and usually greenish. The most abundant honeycreeper is the bananaquit. It is about 4½ in. long and has a dark blue-black back with a white eye-stripe and a bright yellow breast. The green honeycreeper, which is 5 in. long, is one of the largest species. It is bright glossy green with a trace of blue and black on the head. The female is a pale yellowish-green with no black on the head. The male blue dacnis is blue with black on much of the head, back, tail and wings. The female is grass green.

Honeycreepers live in America, from Mexico and Central America through most of South America, and in the West Indies. The most widespread is the bananaquit; it is found throughout the West Indies, except Cuba, and from Mexico to Argentina. Hawaiian honeycreepers are confined to the Hawaiian archipelago and have enchanting local names such as palik and akiapolaau.

Pugnacious honeycreepers

Honeycreepers usually live in flocks in forests or plantations, sometimes mixing with tanagers and other birds. The banana-quit, the most abundant bird in some parts of the West Indies, has become associated with man. It is attracted to sugar put out on verandas or on bird-tables, for which it has to compete with anole lizards and 'Barbados sparrows' which are really lesser Antillean bullfinches. It will also drink from overflow pipes, hanging upside down from the spout while sipping from the trickle of water.

Some honeycreepers seem to be un-necessarily belligerent. The green honey-creeper seizes other small birds that are competing for the same food. AF Skutch, the American ornithologist, saw one attack a tanager without apparent reason and so violently that he ended the attack by throwing a stick at it. Male green honeycreepers have been seen to attack their mates while nest building. The female scarlet-thighed dacnis attacks larger, but harmless thrushes and ground tyrants.

Nectar eaters

The honeycreepers are probably a miscellaneous collection of birds which are united by convergent evolution in feeding on the same food, nectar. Their tongues have brush-like tips similar to those of other nectar-eaters such as the honeyeaters (p 1095). The 'brush' helps to sweep up the nectar. Some honeycreepers, known as flower-piercers, have special bills for piercing the sides of flowers rather than putting their heads down the corolla tubes. The upper part of the bill has a hooked tip and holds the corolla steady while the shorter and very sharp lower half pierces it. The unusually long tongue is then inserted through the hole. Damaging the flowers may cause losses in plantations. The bananaquit some-times damages banana crops because its feet scratch the tiny bananas at the bottom of a bunch while it is feeding at the flowers farther up. When the bananas grow the small scratches become quite noticeable. Some honeycreepers, the blue dacnis and green honeycreeper for example, also feed on fruit and the bananaquit and others eat some insects.

Nest-building to music

Honeycreepers build cup-shaped nests in dense foliage. The nest of the scarlet-thighed honeycreeper is a frail hammock, camouflaged from below by pieces of green fern, but the bananaquit builds a domed nest with the entrance underneath. The female does all the building but she is accompanied by the male on her collecting trips and he sings his feeble song while she is weaving the leaves, grasses and fibres. During this period the male feeds the female and he continues to do so while she is incubating the 3—5 eggs. The eggs hatch out in 12—13 days and the male then helps the female to feed the young.

Hawaiian honeycreepers

The Hawaiian honeycreepers appear to be descended from an ancestor, perhaps a nectar-drinking tanager, that arrived from America 2000 miles away, presumably blown off-course by the wind. From this ancestral type about 22 species evolved. They may be 4—8 in. long and their colours range from green, grey and black to bright red and yellow. Breeding habits are uni-form; simple green nests are built in trees, bushes or long grass and 2 or 3 eggs are laid

Jane Burton: Photo Res

△ *Gourmet at work: head down in the flowers of a yellow Poui tree, a Jamaican bananaquit throws caution to the winds and settles down to a nectar meal.*

in them. The diversity of the Hawaiian honeycreepers lies in their bills and feeding habits. The subfamily Drepanidinae have curved bills and brush-tipped tongues for nectar-drinking and probing for insects. The subfamily Psittirostriinae have short, finch-like bills for eating seeds. There are variations on these bill patterns. Some use their long bills for probing insects out of crevices in bark, while others chisel away bark by hammering it like woodpeckers.

The evolution of different forms and feeding habits of the honeycreeper was aided, like the adaptive radiation of Darwin's finches (p 615), by the absence of competition from other birds. Changes, in both birds, are in feeding rather than breeding habits because the environment for breeding is uniform on both the Galapagos and Hawaii. On the other hand there is a diversity of available food. The diet of different Hawaiian honeycreepers includes nectar, seeds, fruit, spiders and insects.

The first stage in the evolution of the Hawaiian honeycreepers is a diversification of nectar-drinking types. In the tropics nectar-drinkers evolve faster than insect-eaters. Insects are everywhere, but nectar is abundant only locally, so the nectar-drinkers have to travel in search of it. In this way they move to new places where some may become isolated and are able to evolve in a different way from the original stock. They may be isolated on islands or on environmental 'islands' such as mountain tops.

In the last century nearly one quarter of the various kinds of Hawaiian honeycreeper have become extinct. At one time their feathers were used by the Hawaiians in the manufacture of cloaks and it is often said that this caused their extinction, but the downfall of the honeycreepers was really caused by American colonisation. Destruction of the forests, introduced predators and diseases were something that the specialised honeycreepers could not combat.

class	**Aves**
order	**Passeriformes**
family	**Emberizidae**
genera & species	**Chlorophanes spiza** green honeycreeper **Coereba flaveola** bananaquit **Cyanerpes caeruleus** purple honeycreeper **Dacnis cayana** blue dacnis **D. venusta** scarlet-thighed honeycreeper, others
family	**Drepanididae** Hawaiian honeycreepers
genera & species	**Hemignathus wilsoni** akiapolaau **Loxops coccinea** akepa **Vestiaria coccinea** iiwi, others

Left: Delicately camouflaged female and . . .
Centre: Resplendent male purple honeycreepers.
*Below: Blue honeycreeper **Cyanerpes cyaneus**.*

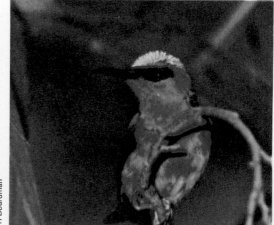

R Boardman

△ *Tool for the job: brown honeyeater* **Lichmera indistincta** *uses its needle-sharp bill on a banana flower (left) and a grevillea blossom (right).*

Honeyeater

*Honeyeaters are a diverse group of birds that eat mainly nectar and fruit. They are very varied in form and habits. The curiously named o-o-aa of Hawaii searches for insects in tree trunks, propping itself on its stiff tail like a woodpecker. The leatherheads or friar-birds resemble jackdaws but several have horny growths on their bills and vulture-like bald heads. The spinebills **Acanthorhynchus** have long curved bills and hover in front of flowers like hummingbirds. Other honeyeaters resemble tits, flycatchers or warblers. They are generally dull looking and some have wattles and lobes or bare patches of skin on the face.*

Half of the 160 honeyeater species live in Australia, the remainder in New Zealand and the islands of the southwest

Pacific. Some reach Hawaii where they are now less common because of the destruction of the natural forests. The o-o, perhaps the shortest named of any bird, is one species that is now extinct. Its yellow feathers, sprouting in tufts like epaulettes from under its wings, were used on royal capes. An o-o has not been seen for over 50 years. The Maoris used the yellow feathers of the stitchbird for ornamental capes in the same way as the Hawaiians used the o-o. Because the forests have been cut down, it is now found only on a small island off New Zealand.

*Very few honeyeaters live outside the Australasian region, which includes New Guinea. The brown honeyeater **Lichmera indistincta** reaches Bali and another lives on the Bonin Islands off Japan. In South Africa there are the two immensely long-*

tailed sugarbirds, isolated and rather different from the rest of the honeyeaters. Although sugarbirds are nectar eaters with the same specialised tongue as the other honeyeaters, it is difficult to see how they got to Africa from the Australasian region. It may be that they are unrelated and that their nectar-eating habits are an example of convergent evolution.

Good singers

Many of the honeyeaters are good singers, but not the ones living in dense forests. The tui is one of the best songsters in New Zealand and is also a good mimic. It has the alternative name of parson bird because of the two patches of white feathers at the neck that look like the 'squares' worn at times by clergymen. Another good performer is the New Zealand bellbird, *Anthornis melanura* which sings in chorus, the notes sounding like the pealing of bells.

Honeyeaters live in a variety of terrains from almost barren country to dense rain forests. The singing honeyeater *Meliphaga virescens* is found in the coastal sand dunes of Australia, but honeyeaters are usually restricted to flowering trees and shrubs and are rarely seen on the ground. Many of them are gregarious, moving around the countryside in groups, sometimes in huge flocks, in search of flowers, berries and fruits. A few species are orchard pests.

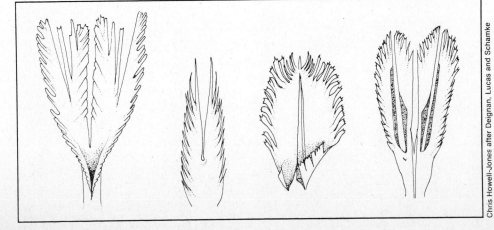

◁ *Most nectar-eaters have very long specialised tongues with brush-like tips. Tongue tips of, left to right: **Dicaeum nigrilore** a flowerpecker (p 787) **Cyanerpes cyanea** an emberizid honeycreeper **Vestiaria coccinea** a drepanidid honeycreeper **Apa opteron** a honeyeater.*

1063

Important pollinators

Some honeyeaters live exclusively on nectar. The stitchbird even feeds its chicks on nothing but nectar, which is unusual. (Insects are usually brought for the chicks to provide them with the protein needed for growth.) Other honeyeaters have largely lost the nectar-eating habit and do not have the 'paintbrush' tongue. The strong-billed honeyeater *Melithreptus validirostris* of Tasmania behaves like a nuthatch, running up tree trunks picking up insects from under the bark. The rufous-throated and rufous-banded honeyeaters hawk for insects like flycatchers (p 791).

Honeyeaters have the same specialized digestive system as the nectar-eating flowerpeckers (p 787). The gizzard can be bypassed, to send food straight into the intestine. The tongue is also modified for nectar eating. The tip is divided into four and each part is 'frayed' to form a delicate brush with which the nectar is swept up. Like the flowerpeckers the honeyeaters also pollinate the flowers they feed on. With the parrots they are responsible for the pollination of most of the flowering trees and shrubs in Australia.

Nesting high in trees

The nest is cup-shaped, sometimes so loosely woven that the eggs can be seen from underneath. It is usually placed high in a tree. Some of the gregarious species nest in colonies of a score or so pairs. An unusual habit has been developed by the blue-faced honeyeater *Entomyzon cyanotis*. It very rarely builds its own nest, but uses the nest of a babbler instead. Sometimes it does not even wait for the nest to be abandoned by the rightful owner but drives it away.

The eggs are incubated for around 18 days and the chicks are fed by both parents for a similar period.

Hair-thieves

Apart from the usual materials such as twigs, grass and flower stems, honeyeaters sometimes incorporate animal hair in their nests, usually as a lining. As impatient as the bluefaced honeyeaters and babblers, they do not always wait for the owner to relinquish the hair. The honeyeaters will boldly settle on the animal of their choice and tweak out hair. The natural source is the hair of native marsupial mammals such as koalas and opossums. Nowadays domestic stock and introduced deer are raided, and occasionally excitement and some consternation are aroused by a honeyeater's attempts to steal human hair.

Honeyeaters are quite fearless thieves, but they do have some difficulties, as AH Chisholm, the Australian ornithologist, recorded. He saw a honeyeater plucking hair from a koala bear. The koala seemed not in the least perturbed until the honeyeater rashly attempted to pull one of the longer hairs of the koala's ears. The koala gave an indignant flick of the head and threw the offender off. Another honeyeater met its match on a bald head. The only hair was on the back and sides and the honeyeater was unable to reach it without sliding down the polished skin of the bald pate, scrabbling for a grip.

Barnabys

class	**Aves**
order	**Passeriformes**
family	**Meliphagidae**
genera & species	***Moho braccatus*** *o-o-aa* ***Notiomystis cincta*** *stitchbird* ***Philemon corniculatus*** *friarbird* ***Promerops cafer*** *Cape sugarbird* ***Prosthemadera novaeseelandiae*** *tui* *others*

*Home in a larder: although it will probably feed its chicks on insects, for the body-building protein in them, this white-cheeked honeyeater **Meliornis niger** has built its nest wisely; the **Dryanda** bush around it is the main nectar supply for the adult birds.*

Honeyguide

The honeyguides are a family of small birds, unusual in both their feeding and breeding habits. They range from sparrow to thrush size, and are related to the barbets (p 141). The plumage is dull, generally brown or grey above and lighter underneath, but some have patches of colour on the tail, wings or head, and the greater honeyguide has yellow wing patches. The most colourful is the orange-rumped honeyguide with golden yellow crown and chin and an orange rump. The lyre-tailed honeyguide has black and white tail feathers that fan out along the length of the tail, and in the other species the outer two pairs of tail feathers are shorter than the rest.

There are 11 species of honeyguide, most of them living in Africa south of the Sahara and the others in southern Asia. One rare species is found in the jungles of Malaya and Borneo.

Wax-eaters

Honeyguides live singly or in pairs in forest and brush country. They are strong fliers, with a rapid undulating flight. They do not migrate but it seems they make seasonal movements in search of food. Honeyguides eat mainly insects which they may catch on the wing, like flycatchers—flying out from a perch, catching an insect, such as a termite, flying ant or fly, and carrying it back to the perch. Locusts are also caught and honeyguides have been found feeding on fruits and berries, but their main food is bees and wasps, especially wild honeybees; honeyguides are rarely found where there are no bees or wasps. The adult bees are caught on the wing and nests are attacked. Honeyguides have a tough skin which may be a protection against stings but there are no records of honeyguides removing the wasp or bee stings before eating them, as do bee-eaters (p 182) and honey buzzards (p 341). It is quite possible that honeyguides are immune to stings because they have been seen disappearing into bees' nests and reappearing apparently unscathed although the bees within buzzed furiously.

They penetrate bees' nests to eat the larvae and, more particularly, the wax from the combs. It was some time before naturalists realised that it was wax, rather than honey, that attracted honeyguides to bees. Wax-eating is a rare habit in birds and honeyguides are unique in the amount of wax they eat. It is a very indigestible substance, but honeyguides have bacteria in their intestines that break it down.

Honeyguides enlist help

It has already been mentioned that honeyguides lure honey badgers to bees' nests and feed on the leftovers after the badgers have torn them open. The evidence for this behaviour is based mainly on the reports of Africans; there are very few eyewitness reports by naturalists. As honeyguides also solicit help from humans, it seems reasonable that they could have learned to co-operate with honey badgers.

Only two, perhaps three, species of honeyguide are known to carry out this quite remarkable behaviour, which seems to be started by the bird finding a nest with bees flying in and out. Abandoned nests with plenty of wax are ignored and new nests, occupied but devoid of wax, are attacked. The honeyguide first attracts the attention of its helper by calling and fanning its tail. The call is a rapid churring like a box of matches being rattled, which is kept up until

A meal to itself: a young greater honeyguide pecks at food few other birds could digest—beeswax.

the follower moves towards it. Then the honeyguide flies towards the bees' nest and perches again until the follower catches up. The process is repeated until the nest is reached, when the honeyguide falls silent while the nest is being torn open.

Laying in others' nests

Breeding habits of some honeyguides are completely unknown, but those honeyguides that have been studied are all parasitic like the cuckoo (p 589). The males sing from special perches within their territories. The females are attracted, mating takes place and the pair splits up, the female departing to find the nest of a suitable host. As well as singing, male lyre-tailed honeyguides perform complicated aerial displays and produce beating sounds rather like the 'drumming' of snipe, caused by the rush of wind vibrating their outer tail feathers.

The female honeyguide lays her eggs in the nests of hole-nesting birds such as barbets, woodpeckers, bee-eaters and kingfishers. She waits until the rightful owners are away and then slips into the nest and lays a single white egg. At the same time the host's eggs are destroyed by being punctured. Any eggs that are laid after the honeyguide egg, are able to hatch out, but the honeyguide chick kills its nestmates. The upper and lower halves of its bill are armed with sharp hooks with which it repeatedly pecks the other chicks until they succumb. When it is about a week old the hooks drop off. The chick then has the undivided attention of its foster parents.

Leading the way

Co-operation between honeyguides and honey badgers or humans is quite surprising. The honeyguide is very persistent and will follow people about if they fail to respond. What is more surprising is that the behaviour should have developed in the first place, when honeyguides are quite capable of obtaining their own beeswax. Presumably the honeyguides have learned to associate an easy meal with animals that habitually tear open bees' nests. It is more difficult to see how the honeyguide developed its leading behaviour and how the honey badger learned to follow it. Unfortunately there are so few observations of honeyguides and honey badgers that we do not really know what happens.

On the other hand, co-operation between honeyguides and man is well known. When out searching for honey Africans will imitate the grunting and growling of honey badgers in an attempt to coax the honeyguides into leading them to a nest. They will make sure to leave some honeycomb for the honeyguide, otherwise, they believe, it will extract revenge by leading them to a venomous snake or lion. There is even a legend that the honeyguide leads man to destroy bees' nests because the bees once judged against the honeyguide over an argument with a mouse.

As the honeyguides are reared under foster-parents and never see their parents, guiding behaviour must be instinctive, but the honeyguides appear to learn which animals are worth guiding. As Africa is becoming more civilized the guiding habit is dying out. Africans are unwilling to risk being stung when they can buy sugar quite cheaply, and without their encouragement the honeyguides are apparently giving up trying to guide them.

class	**Aves**
order	**Piciformes**
family	**Indicatoridae**
genera & species	***Indicator indicator*** *greater honeyguide*
	I. minor *lesser honeyguide*
	I. xanthonotus *orange-rumped honeyguide*
	Melichneutes robustus *lyre-tailed honeyguide, others*

Bjørn Berland

Hooded seal

The hooded seal gets its name from the inflatable proboscis or hood of the male that extends from the nostrils to a point just behind the eyes. It belongs to the same subfamily Cystophorinae, or 'bladder carriers', as the elephant seal (p 713). The inflatable nose of the hooded seal is not quite the same as that of the elephant seal.

Hooded seals are large animals. The adult males grow to a maximum length of around 9 ft and weigh about 900 lb; the females are smaller, about 7 ft, and weigh proportionally less. The adult is dark grey or black in colour with a number of irregular dark markings on the back. These are 2—3 in. across, becoming smaller towards the neck. These markings are often surrounded by a circle of small whitish specks. The seal is paler on the underside, the female being generally paler all over than the male and with less distinct markings.

Hooded seals are largely solitary animals, but they congregate in herds at breeding time. They are found in the North Atlantic and Arctic Oceans, from Newfoundland north around Greenland—especially in the Denmark Strait—and as far north as Spitzbergen and Bear Island. In spite of this comparatively restricted northern range hooded seals occasionally wander far from their normal home. Several have been seen around the British Isles, one as far

Bjørn Berland

Okapia

1066

south as the River Orwell in Suffolk. Vagrant hooded seals have turned up in the Bay of Biscay, while on the other side of the Atlantic they have occurred sporadically as far south as Cape Kennedy in Florida.

The world population of hooded seals has been calculated at 300—500 thousand, but an accurate estimation is difficult on account of their solitary habits. In recent years there has been some change in the population; numbers have increased around Jan Mayen but in the same period have decreased around Newfoundland. It is thought that this may be due to climatic changes in this part of the North Atlantic and Arctic Oceans.

Living on ice

The usual home of the hooded seal is the drift ice of the Arctic Ocean. Towards the end of the summer months the seals are dispersed around the Denmark Strait and at this time they live solitary lives. Very little is known of their movements because of the inaccessibility of the northern seas but they are next seen at the time of the harp seal migrations to the Newfoundland area. The hooded seals stay on the outermost fringes of the pack ice, farther from the land than the harp seals. There they congregate in small family groups and soon afterwards the pups are born, most births taking place from March onwards.

When they leave the ice around Newfoundland the seals move northwards again and they are next seen in the Denmark Strait to the east of Greenland in June and July, when they gather in groups on the ice to moult. After the moult is complete the seals take to the sea again, and from then until they appear off Newfoundland the following year their movements are a mystery. They are not seen in great herds. Probably they just stay feeding in the seas around Greenland.

Mainly fish-eaters

Details of the hooded seal's diet are not very well known except that they are mainly fish-eaters, taking cod, herring and capelin. They also eat mussels, starfish, squid and octopus. Probably like most seals they will feed on whatever happens to be readily available, just as grey seals will feed on cod if they are near a shoal of cod, but are not averse to a meal of salmon if there happen to be salmon conveniently held in nets.

Blue-backed pups

During the breeding period the seals congregate together on the pack ice but they do not found harems as the elephant seal does, but form family groups consisting of one male, one female and her pup. If the pup is threatened they will defend it. At birth the pups are about $3\frac{1}{2}$ ft in length and weigh about 50 lb. They shed a coat of white woolly hair just before they are born (see common seal, p 502) and emerge with a very short-haired, silvery blue coat on the back which is sharply distinct from the creamy white colour of the underside. The pups with this first silvery coat are known as blue-backs. They suckle for only 2—3 weeks, and then the adults mate again and leave the pups to fend for themselves. After they have been abandoned the pups stay on the ice for a further fortnight and then take to the sea themselves.

Polar bear enemies

The hooded seal's greatest enemy is probably the polar bear, which inhabits the same seas. These bears are more danger to the pups than to adults. Man is also an enemy of the hooded seal, the blue-backs being the hunters' main target. Some are hunted by Eskimos who eat the flesh.

Inflatable nose

When the hood of the male is inflated it is about 8—9 in. high and about 12 in. long. It is made up mostly of elastic tissue. There is no lining of blubber under the skin, but inside it is lined by an extension of the nasal membranes and it is also divided down the middle by the nasal septum. The hood itself is inflated by air from the stomach and throat; when it is deflated it hangs down over the end of the nose rather like the proboscis of the elephant seal. It is not quite clear what its function is. Sometimes a very angry seal has been seen to inflate its hood, but on other occasions when seals have been disturbed it has not been inflated. Some seals have also been seen to blow out a red or pink bladder from one nostril but this again only appears occasionally and seals have been seen to blow it out both when irate and also when totally undisturbed. This bladder is only produced from one nostril—usually the left one. It is part of the membrane lining the nostril and it is thought that it is inflated by first inflating the hood. As this collapses the air forces the nasal sac out of one nostril. Occasionally the hooded seal is referred to as the bladdernose on account of its strange habits, about which there is still a great deal to be learnt. This is no easy task with a solitary animal that spends so much of its time either at sea or in the remoter parts of the pack ice.

class	**Mammalia**
order	**Pinnipedia**
family	**Phocidae**
genus & species	*Cystophora cristata*

◁△ *Seal with a bobble on top: a male hooded seal with fully inflated proboscis.*
◁◁◁ *An irate female threatens the photographer. Unlike the male, she has no hood.*
◁◁ *Change of scene: far from the pack-ice, a captive male begs for food.*
◁ *Study in idleness: male at rest.*

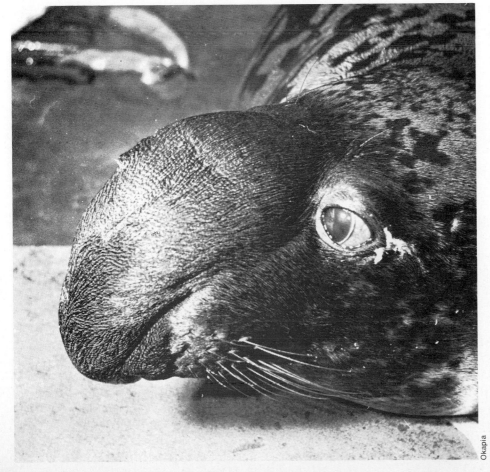

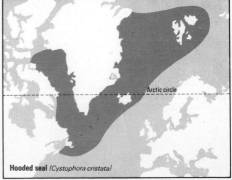

Hooded seal *(Cystophora cristata)*

Okapia

Hookworm

The disease resulting from the parasitic hookworm has plagued mankind for a very long time. There is a reference to this disease—though not to the hookworm itself—in an Egyptian papyrus dated 1500 BC. The full recognition of the parasites themselves did not come until 1843.

*These parasites of man, and of other mammals in the tropics, live in the small intestine, gaining entrance to the body by burrowing through the skin. Like other roundworms or nematodes, a hookworm has an elongated body, circular in cross-section and tapering towards the mouth at the front. The body is not divided into segments and is covered by a tough cuticle. Two species in particular infect man, the pinkish or creamy grey duodenal hookmouth **Ancylostoma duodenale**, about $\frac{1}{2}$ in. long and $\frac{1}{30}$ in. across, and the greyish-yellow American murderer **Necator americanus** which is slightly shorter.*

*The human hookworms flourish in the warmer parts of the world, roughly between the 36th parallel North and the 30th parallel South. **A. duodenale**, the Old World hookworm, occurs particularly in southern Europe, and also along the north coast of Africa, in northern India and in northern China and Japan. It also infects Paraguayan Indians and the Aborigines of Western Australia. **N. americanus**, better adapted to warmer climates, occurs throughout the southern United States, Central America, northern South America and the islands of the Caribbean as well as southern Asia, Melanesia, Polynesia and central and southern Africa. In spite of its name, **N. americanus** is not a native of America but was probably carried there from Africa.*

Cause of anaemia

The adults live on the wall of the small intestine, attached by their horny teeth. Here they feed, either browsing on the mucous membrane or sucking in large amounts of arterial blood with their muscular pharynx. Not surprisingly, a heavy infection of hookworms can cause severe anaemia. Miner's anaemia is due to hookworms which abound in insanitary mines.

Apart from feeding, the chief activity of the females is the laying of large numbers of eggs. *A. duodenale* lays as many as 25 000 each day. The eggs, $\frac{1}{500}$ in. long, are fertilised inside the female by the amoeboid sperm of the slightly smaller males and pass out of the host in its faeces. If conditions are suitable, larvae $\frac{1}{70}$ in. long hatch out in a day or two and feed on bacteria and organic debris. Each larva moults four times, the first moult taking place 3 days after hatching, to reach the second stage larva. This grows to $\frac{1}{5}$ in. and between the fifth and eighth day its mouth becomes sealed off and it moults once again. This time, however, the new larva retains its old cuticle for a while as a loose protective covering. It is at this stage that it is infective. Unable to feed, it lives on stored food reserves, lying in the surface of the soil for up to 15 weeks and climbing upwards when the soil is wet. If it should make contact with human skin, the larva is stimulated to activity and bores its way in, leaving its protective sheath behind. In fact, hookworm larvae do not lie completely inert until touched: they hold the front end of the body up in the air in readiness and are stimulated into great activity by the warmth of a nearby body. The hookworm larva most often enters between the toes, boring into the very small veins to be carried passively in the blood stream to the heart and on to the lungs. Here it starts to burrow again, but this time outwards into the air spaces in the lungs. The next part of its journey is again largely passive. It is carried up the airways by the cilia on the walls of the lungs whose function is to remove dust and debris from these organs. Finally, the larva is coughed up in the sputum and, if this is swallowed, it soon arrives at its destination:

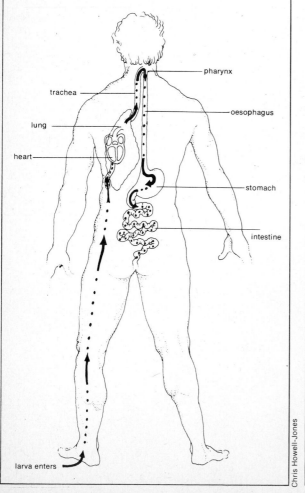

Parasitic pathway of hookworm **Necator americanus**

pharynx
trachea
oesophagus
lung
heart
stomach
intestine
larva enters

Chris Howell-Jones

◁ *Parasite pathway: larva reacts to the warmth of a human foot by boring into it, and rides the blood stream via heart to lungs, then bores into the air spaces in them. Like any foreign matter in the lungs, it is carried in the sputum to the mouth and swallowed. On reaching the small intestine, the larva moults, attaches itself to the wall, moults again and matures in five weeks. Eggs are passed out in the faeces, hatch in one or two days, and restart the cycle.*

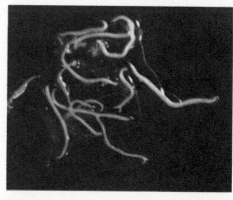

James Webb

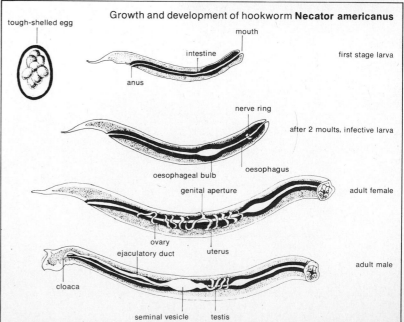

Growth and development of hookworm **Necator americanus**

tough-shelled egg
mouth
intestine
first stage larva
anus
nerve ring
after 2 moults, infective larva
oesophageal bulb
oesophagus
genital aperture
adult female
ovary
uterus
ejaculatory duct
seminal vesicle
testis
cloaca
adult male

Chris Howell-Jones

the small intestine. After moulting again, the larva attaches itself to the wall of the intestine, moults for the last time and becomes a mature adult 5 weeks after entering the body. The majority of worms are eliminated during the next year, but some may survive and remain in the intestine for as long as 16 years.

Insidious disease

As a disease agent, hookworm is more insidious than dramatic even if it can devastate a whole population. A small infection of under 50 worms may pass unnoticed, but a larger one of several hundred may cause serious anaemia and debility as well as diarrhoea alternating with constipation. It was *N. americanus* that was responsible for the condition of the 'shiftless, good-for-nothing, poor trash' of the southern states of America. *A. duodenale* is much more injurious than the other species and harder to expel. Africans suffer less from it than do whites. It is not only the adult worm that is injurious, for invasion of the lungs by larvae may be followed by pneumonia and the attacks on the skin may be accompanied by itching and inflammation. A hookworm of dogs, cats and other carnivores *Ancylostoma braziliense* cannot normally penetrate beyond the germinative layer of the human skin, but may burrow around under the surface for 2−3 months producing an unsightly 'creeping eruption'.

The remedy— sanitation and shoes

Adult worms can be expelled from the intestine with various medicines known as vermifuges, but successful control of hookworm depends much more on an understanding of its life cycle. Wide attention was first directed to hookworms in 1880. Labourers in the Saint Gotthard tunnel in the Swiss Alps suffered badly and then spread the worms to many mines in western Europe. The full life history was not worked out until 1896-7 by Arthur Looss whose key discovery came when he accidentally infected himself by spilling larvae on his skin.

Knowledge of its life history has yielded two basic, and highly effective, rules for the combating of hookworm: the use of proper latrines or other methods of sanitation and the wearing of shoes. Observance of these principles has dramatically reduced the incidence of hookworm in many areas. More detailed information reveals other factors that can influence its incidence. Thus, heavy infections are rare in regions of low rainfall and of heavy clay soil in which the larvae cannot thrive. The larvae flourish best in shady places. From these they may be spread to some extent by trickling rainwater and also by insects, as well as by such animals as pigs and dogs which may eat them in human faeces and void them elsewhere

still alive. Cockroaches may swallow them too, but, in contrast, they probably help to keep down infection, as they do in some Indian mines, since the worms are crushed in the gizzard.

phylum	**Aschelminthes**
class	**Nematoda**
order	**Strongyloidea**
family	**Ancylostomidae**
genera & species	***Ancylostoma caninum*** in dog, jackal, wolf, fox, tiger, rarely in man ***A. ceylanicum*** sometimes in man ***A. duodenale*** in cat, tiger, man, rarely in pig ***Necator americanus***, in pig, rhinoceros, gorilla, and man

▽◁◁ *Adult hookworms shown against dark background on microscope slide (2½ × life size).*
▽◁ *One of the millions of hookworm eggs to pass out of an infected animal, 500 × life size. In ideal conditions it will hatch in one or two days, and the larva will become infective after two moults.*
▽ *Hookworm larva at the infective stage, 150 × life size. If it penetrates human skin it will take 3−5 days to reach the intestine.*

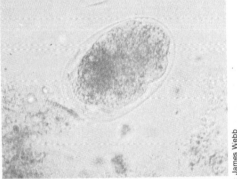
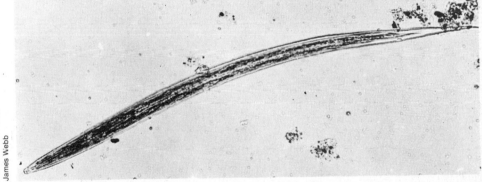

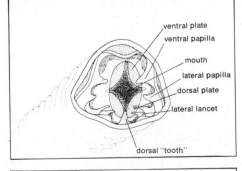

◁ *The business end: mouth capsule of* **Necator americanus.** *Once in the gut the worm attaches itself to the wall, using dorsal 'tooth', dorsal plates and ventral plates, and begins to feed. The grisly meal is sliced from the lining cells of the small intestine by a second line of sharpness: lancets set a little way back, near the mouth. Although the worm feeds mainly on tissue, it breaks many tiny blood vessels as it feeds, causing bleeding and consequently anaemia.*
◁▽ *Intrusion: hookworm larvae entering the body. Apart from direct piercing and burrowing (shown each side of the hairs) they use every crack and pore of the skin to full advantage. In the diagram they are reaching the blood via the gap between hair and skin.*

ventral plate
ventral papilla
mouth
lateral papilla
dorsal plate
lateral lancet
dorsal "tooth"

■ **Old World hookworm**
(*Ancylostoma duodenale*)

× (*A. braziliense*)

▨ **New World hookworm**
(*Necator americanus*)

Hoopoe

At first sight the hoopoe is not quite the magnificent bird that is depicted in pictures. The fan-shaped crest lies folded over the head except when the hoopoe is excited. Nevertheless, its plumage is very handsome. It is pinkish-brown except for the conspicuous black and white bars on the lower back and wings. The tail is black with a white bar at the base; and the hallmark of the hoopoe is the crest of chestnut, black-tipped feathers. The bird is 1 ft long with a bill that is 2 in. long, curved and slender.

The hoopoe lives in most of the Old World. It breeds throughout Europe except in the British Isles and Scandinavia, reaching as far north as the Gulf of Finland. From there its northernmost range runs across to Lake Baikal and the Amur. South of this line it is found over Asia, except Korea and the Indus valley, as far south as Malaysia. In Africa hoopoes are found over most of the continent, including Madagascar, except the Sahara desert and the rain forests of Central Africa. In summer they may wander as far north as Iceland and Spitzbergen, but not to breed.

Rare visitor

Hoopoes prefer warm dry climates with open woodland where they can perch on branches and descend to feed on the ground. They also visit orchards and gardens. The hoopoes living in the north migrate south in winter, the European population moving to Africa. When the climate was warmer hoopoes used to breed farther north; they bred in Denmark until 1876. Now they are rarely seen in the British Isles, although their distinctive plumage never lets them go overlooked as they descend to a lawn to feed.

The name of the hoopoe is derived from its rather cuckoo-like call and has resulted in the scientific name of *Upupa epops*. But, like the crest, the call is not quite as it is described. The hoopoe does not speak its name like the cuckoo but utters a low three syllable 'hoop-hoop-hoop'. In the breeding season the call is accompanied by a fluffing out of the neck feathers and bowing.

Probing for food

Hoopoes feed on the ground, flying to cover on slow, butterfly-like wingbeats. Their long curved bills are used to probe the soil for insects and their larvae, large grubs such as cockchafer grubs, spiders, worms, large centipedes and occasionally lizards. In the winter they also eat ant-lions and termites.

Nesting in holes

Eggs are laid in holes in trees and in buildings, sometimes under piles of stones. Occasionally a rough structure of grass or feathers is made, but otherwise the eggs are laid on the floor of the hole or crevice. Five to eight light grey to olive eggs are laid and incubated by the female alone for 18 days. Their colour soon changes because

Grub up: a parent hoopoe brings food for the family, in the shape of a larva tweaked from the earth with the long bill. The photograph shows a fine example of bird landing technique; after gliding in on a fairly flat path, the hoopoe has extended all available wing space to stay airborne and is lowering the air brakes—back edges of wings—ready to flip the legs forward and land at minimum speed.

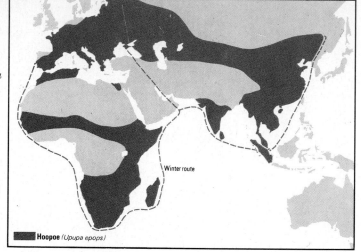

Winter route

Hoopoe *(Upupa epops)*

the female never leaves the nest. All her food is brought by the male. Meanwhile a pile of droppings builds up in the nest hole, staining the eggs. Moreover, the female has an unpleasant odour derived from an oily secretion from the preen gland. Apart from spreading this over her feathers during preening both the female hoopoe and the chicks can eject the oil as a musky spray when frightened. At first the female broods the almost naked young while the male brings food for them in his bill. Later both parents feed the chicks which leave the nest in 3–4 weeks.

Looking fierce

Although apparently slow fliers, hoopoes can move at a surprising speed and can elude trained falcons flying above them, where the falcon cannot dive at them. They also have a strange display, used, apparently, to scare away birds of prey. On seeing a hawk, a hoopoe spreads its wings and tail displaying the bold black and white stripes. At the same time the head is raised and the bill pointed into the air.

Hoopoes have long been persecuted because of their alleged medicinal properties and their recent disappearance from Greece and Crete has been attributed to this.

Wisdom of Solomon

It is not surprising that such a striking bird as the hoopoe should repeatedly appear in folklore. The Ancient Egyptians held it in great esteem, its head being used as a hieroglyph. It appears prominently in Aristophanes' *The Birds*. One tradition tells how hoopoes originally bore crests of gold and this led to their being killed. The hoopoes petitioned King Solomon, as he could understand the language of animals, to ask for divine help. As a result the hoopoes were granted crests of feathers instead of gold.

class	**Aves**
order	**Coraciiformes**
family	**Upupidae**
genus & species	***Upupa epops***

△ *Elevation . . . side view of a gaily coloured leafhopper* **Graphocephala coccinea** ▽ *. . . and plan:* **Cicadella viridis** *shows its pastel wing cases.*

Hopper

There are several thousand species of hoppers belonging to the families commonly called froghoppers, leafhoppers, treehoppers, plant hoppers and jumping plant lice. These insects are related to cicadas and aphides. All are small, most of them are tiny. They are, however, of great economic importance because they suck sap from plants, causing them to wilt, and many inject viruses into the plants, causing diseases.

Froghoppers and cuckoo-spit
In Britain the cuckoo arrives in April on migration from Africa. Soon after it arrives blobs of spittle begin to appear on plants. An ancient belief, still held today in some rural districts, is that the cuckoos have been spitting, giving the name cuckoo spit to these blobs of bubbly froth. In America these are called spittlebugs. Inside each blob of foam is a froghopper nymph, a tiny pale-brown insect with a large head. Sinking its proboscis into the skin of the plant it sucks sap at such a rate that the liquid quickly passes through its digestive tube and out at the other end. There it mixes with a soapy fluid given out from glands on the underside of the abdomen. The sides of the abdominal segments are extended to curve beneath the body enclosing a cavity into which the spiracles open. This chamber opens to the rear through a valve and the froth or spume is caused by expelled air coming into contact with the fluid passing over the valve.

The adult froghopper does not make any froth but leaps from plant to plant. Its large head and jumping powers strongly resemble those of a frog, and earn it the name froghopper *Philaenus spumarius*. Most froghoppers are sombrely coloured but one British species *Cercopis vulnerata*, living on sallows and alders, is a striking black and red. British froghoppers are usually $\frac{1}{4}$ in. long but elsewhere they may reach $\frac{1}{2}$ in.

Leafhopper sharpshooters
These are small insects, rarely more than $\frac{1}{2}$ in. long, but they are serious pests in many parts of the world, damaging a wide variety of cultivated plants, including fruit and other crops. Most of them are powerful jumpers. Some are known as sharpshooters from the way they shoot drops of clear liquid, or honeydew, from the tip of the abdomen, regularly every second for as long as 2 minutes. Because the liquid is sweet ants are attracted to it. Leafhoppers are also known as dodgers. Instead of leaping to safety when disturbed a leafhopper may run round to the other side of a leaf or twig then return quickly to see if all is clear, retreating rapidly again if it is not. Leafhoppers are pests on rice, potatoes, beet, grain, grass and soft fruits. The females use a sharp ovipositor to lay eggs in long rows just under the skin of plants.

Lerps—the jumping plant lice
Another bothersome type of insect, especially on apple and pear trees, is the lerps or jumping plant lice, *Psylla pyricola* and *P. mali*. After passing the winter as eggs, laid the previous autumn on leaf scars, the nymphs, by sucking sap, damage fruit blossom and stunt shoots. They give out their honeydew in long slender waxy tubes. When these break up the honeydew spreads over the leaves of the food-plants. In Australia the Aborigines collect and eat the

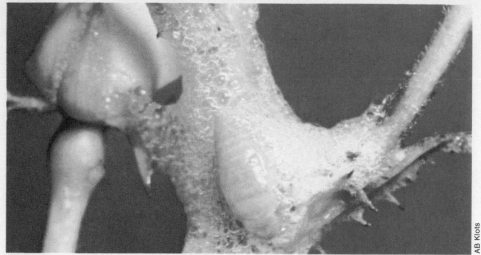

honeydew of the lerps that live on mimosa and eucalyptus.

Plant hoppers

There are over 5 000 species of insects under this heading which are sometimes grouped as one family, sometimes split into a number of families. Collectively they have been known as lantern flies because one of the most striking of them, *Laternaria phosphorea*, was supposed to be luminous. The Chinese candlefly *Fulgora candelaria* is also said to be luminous. In fact, none of them is luminescent. Many have large heads, often grotesquely shaped, and some are brightly coloured while others are covered with white wax that may hang like wool on their bodies. *Laternaria* has a head like a peanut, almost the same size as the body, with the eyes set far back, and the markings on it make it look like a miniature crocodile's head. There is almost certainly protection in the colours of the African species of *Flata*. These have two colour forms, green and red, that live together. Moreover they arrange themselves on a plant stem in a row, the red individuals lowermost looking like blossoms, the green ones above looking like unopened buds.

△ *Hopper 'spit': a larva pierces a twig to feed; excess sap on breathing tubes makes the foam.*
▽ *A treehopper shows disruptive camouflage.*
▽▽ *A leaf? A plant hopper, genus* **Acanalonia**.

Hoppers in the trees

The last group in this cavalcade of hoppers is the treehoppers. Like the froghoppers and the others in this series they feed on sap as nymphs and adults and are noted for their jumping ability. Most of them are not present in large enough numbers to be pests. One, the buffalo treehopper *Ceresa bubalis*, may damage fruit trees through laying eggs in holes in the bark. Each hole is made by the female's ovipositor. As nymphs most treehoppers are inconspicuous but many, especially those in tropical America, have

AB Klots

grotesque shapes. The external skeleton of the front part of the thorax becomes much enlarged and takes on fanciful shapes. In the thornbug *Umbonia crassicornis* it has the shape of a large rose thorn. Sometimes these bugs line up on a twig and can hardly be distinguished from a row of thorns.

Evolution run wild

Is it useful to the treehopper to look like a thorn? Even if the lantern fly does not deceive its enemies by looking like a miniature crocodile, perhaps its outsize proboscis may be protective, by making enemies hesitate before attacking. Treehoppers like *Membracis expansa* have a huge boldly and garishly coloured shield covering the body like a large cap so the insect resting on a plant looks like a flower. In others this outgrowth of the skeleton becomes truly monstrous, forming all manner of odd shapes decorated with spines, or forming a circular arch high above the insect's body. The limit seems reached in one that has an arm rising from the thorax, curving over the head to end in a slender stalk bearing three balls, like the pawnbroker's sign. It is hard to see how such elaborate ornaments benefit the insect. They may be only the result of evolution having run slightly wild.

phylum	**Arthropoda**
class	**Insecta**
order	**Hemiptera**
sub-order	**Homoptera**
families	**Cercopidae** *froghoppers*
	Chermidae *jumping plant lice*
	Fulgoridae *plant hoppers*
	Jassidae *leafhoppers*
	Membracidae *treehoppers*

△ *Either a mobile lump of bark, the head of another animal or a treehopper.*

▽ *Thorn or prey?* **Thelia maculata** *makes predator problems.* ▽ ▽ *Problem magnified.*

Hornbill

Hornbills are so called because of their huge and often bizarre bills that in some species have a large casque giving them an unwieldy top-heavy appearance. The casque, which is larger in males than females, is usually very light, being made up of sponge-like bone, and hornbills are by no means clumsy. That of the Malayan helmeted hornbill, however, is solid bone and is used in carvings. Another peculiarity is the stiff eyelashes, especially of the ground hornbills, which have red patches of skin on face and throat instead of a casque. The rufous-necked hornbill of India also lacks a casque and has blue skin on the face, and scarlet skin on the throat as well as a striking plumage. Hornbills vary in size between the turkey-sized ground hornbill which is 5 ft long with a 5ft wingspan and the red-billed dwarf hornbill that is only 15 in. long.

The range of the hornbills extends through Africa south of the Sahara, but excluding Madagascar, and across tropical Asia from southern Arabia to the Solomon Islands and Philippines.

△ *Ethiopian freak: the gnarled face of a ground hornbill.*

△▷ *Dowdy but still unique: a female black and white casqued hornbill.*

◁ *Out on a limb: a ground hornbill runs an idle eye over the surrounding countryside.*

▷ *Not so much a beak, more a head-borne ornament:* **Buceros** *carries less weight than it looks; like nearly all hornbills, it has a casque of light honeycombed bone.*

▽ *Home with the spoils: a yellow-billed hornbill prepares to do justice to an outsize in caterpillars.*

▽▷ *Captive dejection: a male wreathed hornbill*

◁ *Where there are hot, wet jungles, there are hornbills, except in the New World, where their place is taken by the toucans — remarkably similar birds, giving an example of convergent evolution.*

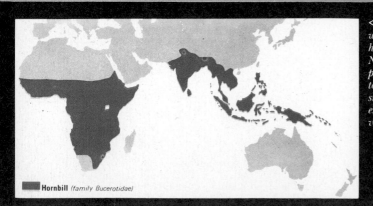

■ **Hornbill** *(family Bucerotidae)*

Legendary bird

The habits of most hornbills are not well known despite their strange appearance and even stranger breeding habits. Hornbills feature prominently in folklore and from early times Europeans have brought back strange tales about them. Folklore and superstition often prevented hornbills from being killed but nowadays their forest homes are being cut down and they are being deprived of the large trees they need for nesting. An exception is the ground hornbill that lives in savannah country.

One hornbill that has been studied in detail is the silvery-cheeked hornbill of East Africa. It feeds in flocks often commuting some distance between feeding grounds and roosts, where 100 or more spend the night roosting together in tall trees. On their way to and fro hornbills fly in small parties making a considerable amount of noise. Apart from loud cries, roars and bellows many of them make sounds like the puffing of a steam engine, caused by air rushing through gaps in the wings where the plumage feathers do not cover the bases of the flight feathers.

Mainly fruit-eaters

Hornbills feed largely on fruits such as figs, passion fruit and various berries which are collected by hopping about the larger limbs of trees. The larger hornbills can swallow palm nuts and in southeast Asia hornbills eat the fruit of nux vomica and related plants that contain strychnine. The hornbills are safe because they do not crack the seeds that contain the strychnine. Some hornbills feed largely on insects. Termites are a favourite food and a wide range of larger animals are caught, including lizards and once a hornbill was seen with a bat but this escaped. Nests are robbed for their eggs and young chicks, and hornbills regularly frequent forest fires to catch the animals fleeing from them. The white-crested hornbill often follows troops of monkeys through the forests of West Africa feeding on the insects they disturb, and others follow army ant columns for the same reason.

Hornbills also attack snakes, sometimes several hornbills banding together to kill one large snake. The hornbills rain blows on the prey with their large, sharp-edged bills, at the same time shielding themselves with their wings. This seems to be an instinctive way of attacking such reptiles because a young tame hornbill immediately attacked a toy rubber snake, holding one wing forward as a shield.

Walling up the wife

Apart from the ground hornbills which nest among rocks or in tree stumps, hornbills nest in hollow trees, sometimes using abandoned woodpecker holes. After the eggs have been laid the female blocks up the entrance of the hollow with a wall until there is only a narrow slit left, with herself inside. She is then fed by the male passing food through the slit. It is this habit that has gained the hornbill its place in folklore; among some tribes of Africa it is a symbol of marital fidelity.

The walling-up behaviour varies from species to species. Sometimes the male

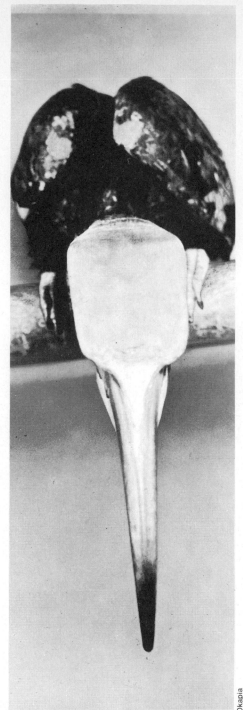

Looking like an acute case of loss of balance an inquisitive hornbill leans downwards to investigate happenings below. Female hornbills at least are no newcomers to captivity; they wall themselves into their own nests after the eggs have been laid, and then break down the barrier of hardened mud when they hatch, to help the male feed the young. If the mother has a large clutch, she breaks out early, and the chicks rebuild the wall.

helps collect material or builds the wall, while in other species the female imprisons herself unaided. The female silvery-cheeked hornbill builds the wall from the inside with a plaster of mud and saliva that is brought by the male, while other species use dung or clay. While she can the female squeezes through the gap in the wall, but when it is

reduced to a slit she is completely imprisoned and must rely on the male to bring food. He props himself against the trunk, using his tail as a 'shooting stick', and regurgitates food, as many as 60 fruits at one visit. One male was seen to bring 24 000 fruits to his mate during the nesting season. The male may also bring bark and flowers but why he should do this is not known.

The usual clutch is 3—5 eggs, but the larger hornbills may lay only 1 or 2. Incubation lasts 1—2 months and the chicks take 6—7 weeks to fledge. Some females stay in the nest until the young are ready to fly, while others with larger clutches break out and help the male with the feeding. In such instances the half-grown chicks rebuild the wall after the mother has left—a most remarkable piece of behaviour. When the time comes for the chicks to leave the nest the wall is broken down and the chicks fly out, some with the encouragement of the parents who may tip them out.

Confinement problems

The value of this strange nesting habit is presumably to prevent the nest being robbed. No doubt it is very successful, as the wall sets rock-hard and any enemy trying to get through has to contend with the powerful bill of the female hornbill within. During her imprisonment she moults her feathers extremely rapidly, so for a short time she is without her flight feathers. This does not matter unless the nest is broken open and then she is helpless. To reduce the crush in the nest both the female and the baby hornbills sit with their tails folded over their backs, but there is a more serious problem; nest sanitation. Although a hornbill may spend 4 months in its nest it emerges quite clean, as do the chicks. The problems of nest sanitation have not been fully studied but it is known that fruit stones are cast out and the excreta is ejected forcibly through the slit. Insects such as bagworms, beetle larvae and cockroaches are found in hornbill nests and they may play an important part in clearing up debris. More observations must be made, however, before the whole story of the hornbills' strange nesting habits is known.

class	**Aves**		
order	**Coraciiformes**		
family	**Bucerotidae**		
genera & species	*Aceros nipalensis* rufous-necked hornbill *Bucorvus leadbeateri* ground hornbill *Bycanistes brevis* silvery-cheeked hornbill *Tockus camurus* red-billed dwarf hornbill *Tropicranis albocristatus* white-crested hornbill others		

Horned frog

Some horned frogs are hornless, some are armoured, but they all have a reputation for pugnacity. Their numbers seem to be controlled largely by cannibalism.

The horned frog is a large amphibian up to 10 in. long and unusually wide. It has a big, bulky head with a wide mouth. The body is handsomely, even garishly, ornamented with geometrical patterns of green and yellow or rusty red and yellow on a blackish ground colour. The skin is covered with warts on the upper parts and is finely granular on the underside. In some species the eyelids are drawn out into what look like small horns. These are, however, only flaps of skin, neither hard nor sharp. Nevertheless, they add to the grotesque and somewhat forbidding appearance of these frogs.

The dozen or so species all live in Central and South America, as far south as Argentina. There are also several horned frogs in southeast Asia.

Puzzle over their colours

Horned frogs are, in places, abundant near rivers and swamps and after rain are seen crawling through the grass in large numbers. At other times they lie buried in soft ground or among leaf litter with only the back and head exposed. In spite of their striking colours they are hard to see so long as they remain still. They give an example of how difficult it is sometimes to decide the value of an animal's colours. Lifted from its natural surroundings the horned frog's colours are conspicuous, yet their disruptive pattern is one we always associate with camouflage. Moreover, some people claim that their bright colours are warning colours, and we know from experience with other animals that a warning coloration is something flaunted to warn off would-be attackers — the reverse of camouflage.

Ferocious frogs

Whatever the meaning of its colours the fact remains that a horned frog, in marked contrast with most other frogs, is highly belligerent. People have told of having horned frogs in captivity that leaped at them when they went to feed them, biting their fingers and hanging on like a bulldog. This is probably no more than the frogs' normal way of feeding, for the adults do not go in search of food but lie half-buried waiting for prey to come near. They then seize their victims, even jumping out from their hiding place to do so. Their prey is almost anything moving they can swallow: insects, frogs, lizards, even snakes, small birds and small mammals. They are thought to be strongly cannibalistic and this may control their numbers, for they have few enemies. In addition, the Wied's horned frog of Brazil has a dense bony

Horned frogs are said not to be venomous but it would be surprising if the many warts on their bodies were not able to give out a poison of the kind found in toads. Their aggressive actions help no doubt to deter some enemies. In addition, the Wied's horned frog of Brazil has a dense bony

△ *Cold-blooded power:* **Megophrys.**

Peter Ward

△ *That hungry look:* **Ceratophrys ornata.**
▽ *Camouflaged but pugnacious:* **C. calcarata.**

SC Bisserot

John Tashjian at Steinhart Aquarium

shield covering the head and part of the back, which might make it hard to deal with.

More ferocious frogs

In southeast Asia there are other species known as horned frogs, but they belong to a separate family. This means they differ from the South American horned frogs in their anatomy but resemble them in outward appearance. They have a 'horn' on each eyelid and have wide mouths and strong jaws like the South American species. They are also strongly cannibalistic and have a bony shield covering the head and part of the back. So the horned frogs of America and southeast Asia give us yet another good example of convergent evolution in which unrelated animals having the same way of life are superficially alike.

Two contrasting tadpoles

The two groups of horned frogs differ, however, in the behaviour of the tadpole. Those of the South American horned frogs are predatory from the start, feeding on other small animals. The tadpoles of the southeast Asia horned frogs are vegetarians. Some of them have large funnel-like mouths by which they hang vertically from the surface film of the water. Their mouths are armed with rows of minute horny teeth which act as rasps to scrape algae and other small growths from the leaves of waterplants.

Horse-killers?

The horned frogs of southeast Asia look as grotesque as those of South America. One addition they have is a spine — a pointed flap of skin — on the snout, which makes them look more formidable than they are. Guenther's horned frog, of South America, also has a 'spine' of skin on its snout that looks like a sting. Even those that lack these nasal ornaments look fearsome enough to have earned them a bad reputation. When their pugnacity is added to this the way is open for exaggerated ideas. One of these, from the Argentine, is that the *escucrzo*, as it is called there, may bite the lip of a grazing horse and that the horse will die from the bite. From what we know of horned frogs it is easy to believe that it would not hesitate to snap at a horse. Even a young horned frog, less than an inch across, will make quite a show at attacking. And even if the horned frog's mouth contains no venom, it is not impossible that its teeth might leave a wound that becomes septic, so causing the death of a horse.

class	**Amphibia**		
order	**Salientia**		
family	**Leptodactylidae (S America)**		
genus & species	***Ceratophrys appendicula*** *Guenther's horned frog* ***C. stolzmanni*** *escucrzo* ***C. varia*** *Wied's horned frog* *others*		
family	**Pelobatidae (SE Asia)**		
genus	***Megophrys***		

*An optician's nightmare: a horned toad **Phrynosoma coronatum** after a demonstration of its unsavoury but decidedly startling defence mechanism.*

Horned toad

The horned toad is not a toad as the name suggests but a lizard with the face of a toad. If it were larger it could be mistaken for a prehistoric reptile. As it is, its main claim to fame is its alleged ability to squirt blood out of its eyes.

It can measure up to 5 in. long, and has a squat, flattened, almost circular body, short legs and short tail. The head is ornamented with backwardly directed spines, the so-called horns, and the back is covered with smaller spines. Some have been called short-horned, because the head spines are not prominent, others are called long-horned. In both types the body is covered in small scales, as is usual in lizards, but there are larger thornlike scales as well. Usually the edges of the body are ornamented with large flat scales.

There are a dozen species of horned toads or horned lizards ranging from just over the Canadian border southwards through the western United States to Mexico. The most widely distributed is the Texas horned toad, from Nebraska in the north to Chihuahua and Sonora in Mexico.

Toad-like behaviour

These lizards live in deserts and semi-desert sandy country, from low-lying ground to 10 000 ft altitude. They drink dew and hunt insects, particularly ants. A horned toad moves slowly towards its prey and, when close enough, stops and bends its head slightly towards it. Then it shoots out a thick tongue and in a flash carries the insect back into its mouth. As the day wanes the horned toad buries itself in the warm sand. It pushes its blunt snout into the sand and by wriggling strenuously makes a furrow in which it lies half buried, or with only the top of the head showing. As autumn approaches, the horned toad spends more and more time buried and in winter it buries itself deeper and goes into a torpid state.

Egg-layers and live-bearers

Most horned lizards are egg-layers. Between April and July the female digs a hole 6 in. deep in the sand. She does this with her forefeet, pushing the sand back with her hindfeet. She lays up to 30 yellowish-white, oval, tough-shelled eggs each ½ in. long, in the hole. These she covers with sand and leaves. The eggs hatch up to 90 days later, the time varying with the species. A few horned lizards bear live young, up to 30 at a time. These are from eggs that hatch just before being laid. The young measure 1¼ in. at hatching.

A dangerous mouthful

Horned toads have few enemies because of their armour and the camouflage effect of their colours. Snakes sometimes eat them and often pay for this with their lives since the horns of the lizard may penetrate the wall of the snake's gullet. They are also well camouflaged, for not only do the lizards bury themselves in the sand, but the mottled colours on their bodies tend to take on the colour or pattern of the sand or gravel on which they are living.

Blood-squirters

Horned toads are said to squirt blood from their eyes when alarmed. Yet there are many who have kept the lizards as pets or are used to seeing them around who say this is untrue. It is clear from all the evidence that they do this but in a curiously erratic way. Raymond L Ditmars, American specialist in the study of reptiles, handled several hundred horned toads before he saw one squirt blood from its eyes. Another American specialist, Winton, writing in 1914, tells how one of his students stooped to pick up a horned toad and received a splash of blood on his hand which spread in a fan-shaped smear from the second joint of the index finger to the wrist. Winton saw three toads do this. All were males and all were sloughing their skins at the time. In each, the eye from which the blood was ejected showed a small quantity of clotted blood in the back of the cornea, in which the blood vessels were swollen although the cornea itself remained intact. So it seems one person may handle three of the lizards and see the blood-letting three times, while another may handle hundreds over a period of years and never see it.

The usual explanation is that this action is defensive, and that the blood is an irritant to the eyes of small mammals. Another suggestion is that it may be connected with the breeding season, although nobody is very clear how. A third suggestion is that it may be due to a parasite, and a fourth is that it may be a secondary use acquired by relatively few individuals.

This habit is not unique, however, only particularly spectacular. It is like the 'blood-spitting' of the dwarf boas of the West Indies. And few authors, even specialist authors in books devoted to snakes, ever mention this.

class	**Reptilia**
order	**Squamata**
suborder	**Sauria**
family	**Iguanidae**
genus & species	*Phrynosoma douglassi* *P. m'calli* others

Hornet

The name 'hornet' should really be used for a large species of social wasp living in Europe and rarely found in well wooded districts of southern Britain. In North America the name is applied to a large native wasp, the white-faced hornet, as well as to the European species, which has been introduced. The common American social wasps of the genus **Dolichovespula**, popularly known as yellowjackets, and large social wasps in the tropics are also sometimes called hornets. In the rest of the English-speaking world 'hornet' has lost all precise meaning and is applied to any large social wasp, rather as 'tarantula' describes any large spider.

The European hornet is distinguished from the two almost identical common wasps, **Vespula vulgaris** and **Vespula germanica**, and other similar species, by its larger size and distinct coloration, which is dull orange and brown instead of bright yellow and black. Worker hornets are rather larger than queen wasps, and the queen hornet is over an inch long.

Papier-mâché nests

The European hornet resembles the common wasps in that it makes a 'paper' nest of wood chewed to a paste, but the nest is usually built in a hollow tree, occasionally under a bank or in an unfrequented building and for this reason alone often escapes notice. Wasps use hard sound wood to make their paper, but hornets are less particular and content themselves with soft decayed wood sometimes mixing it with sand or soil. The resultant paper is yellowish and rather coarse in texture. The nest is of the usual wasp type, made up of a series of tiers or layers of cells, separated by interspaces, with the cells opening downwards. The cells in a hornets' nest are larger but less numerous than in a wasps' nest, and the total population of a hornet colony is smaller.

Its large size and alarming appearance have led to the hornet acquiring a reputation for ferocity which does it great injustice. It is in fact less aggressive than the common wasps and will not sting unless seriously molested. It has the unusual habit among wasps of remaining partly active at night. It sometimes goes to the treacle bait that collectors paint on tree trunks to attract the moths that fly at night, giving the collector quite a surprise when he finds a colourful hornet in his trap instead of a drab moth.

Laying the foundation

The life-history of the hornet is essentially the same as that of the common wasp. Fertile females or queens appear in the nest towards the end of summer. They mate and then find a sheltered place in which to hibernate, while all the other inhabitants of the nest, males and infertile females or workers, die. In the spring the queens become active again and search for nesting sites, each one founding a separate nest or colony. The queen begins the paper nest by building a single tier of downward-pointing cells hanging by a stalk from the roof of a cavity. In each cell she lays an egg and the eggs hatch into larvae which she feeds until they grow to full size and pupate, each in its own cell. These pupae produce a small brood of workers.

From then on the energies of the queen are devoted to laying more and more eggs in cells built by the workers, which enlarge the nest as their numbers increase. They also forage for themselves as well as for the larvae and the queen. In the late summer queens and males are reared and the cycle begins all over again. As in other social wasps the larvae are fed on animal food, such as flies and caterpillars, and the adults live mainly on nectar, honeydew and other sweet juices from plants.

Face to face with a hornet. Despite its intimidating look, this European hornet does not seek trouble and is less aggressive than the common wasp.

GE Hyde

Moths mimic hornets

A familiar theory of protective mimicry, originally founded on the study of tropical American butterflies, can be given here. Two moths, the hornet moth *Sesia apiformis* and the lunar hornet moth *Sphecia bembeciformis,* of the family Sesiidae or clearwings are as big as a hornet, have transparent wings and yellow and brown banded bodies. They look so like hornets that few people will touch them and birds are probably deceived as well. Birds avoid eating wasps and hornets both on account of their stings and because they have an unpleasant taste.

phylum	**Arthropoda**
class	**Insecta**
order	**Hymenoptera**
family	**Vespidae**
genus & species	**Vespa crabro** *European hornet* **Vespula maculata** *white-faced hornet* *others*

▷ *What the proverbial 'hornets' nest' looks like: an irregularly-ridged papier-mâché ball suspended in the undergrowth, patrolled by its outsize inmates.*
▽ *Solitary diner: European hornet* **Vespa crabro** *feeding on a flower.*

Okapia

GS Giacomelli

Horse

Wild horses, as distinct from asses and zebras which also belong to the genus *Equus*, were widespread over Europe and Asia in prehistoric times. Early in the historic period their numbers were much reduced through being hunted for their flesh and for domestication. Only two remnants of what must have been big populations of wild horses persisted. One, the tarpan, survived in the Ukraine until 1851. The other is Przewalski's horse, also called the Mongolian wild horse, of Central Asia, which almost became extinct. The domesticated horse must have been from one or both of these, but when and how this happened is unknown. The best we can say is that the horse was domesticated at some time before 2 000 BC.

The rough-tough tarpan

All that remains of the tarpan is two skulls, a drawing, some cave paintings and a description by Johann Friedrich Gmelin, a German naturalist who visited the Ukraine in 1769 expressly to find the tarpan. He described it as small, a very shy and very swift animal with a long, mouse-coloured coat, dark feet, pointed ears, fiery eye, erect mane and tail covered with hair. The loss of the tarpan was partly due to hunting and partly through dilution — that is, by hybridizing with domesticated horses. Gmelin told how these wild horses were a nuisance through coming into the fields to eat the hay stooked for carting, two of them eating a stook in one night. He also told how the wild stallions lured domestic mares away after defeating the domestic stallions in bloody fights that often ended in the death of the tame stallions. Small horses painted on the walls of Palaeolithic caves at Lascaux, in France, are also believed to be tarpans.

Mongolian wild horses

Przewalski's horse was discovered by Nicolai Przewalski, Russian explorer, in 1881, in Central Asia. At that time they seemed to have been numerous but numbers decreased in the disturbed times following the Revolution of 1918. It is believed that 40 of them survived this but experts on this horse suggest that even these had been diluted by breeding with domestic horses. Even so, efforts are now being made to protect the surviving stock in the wild and preserve this horse in zoos. Przewalski's horse is stocky, 4½ ft at the shoulder, sandy-orange brown with a black erect mane, no forelock and a longhaired black tail. The summer coat has a dark stripe down the middle of the back. There is an indistinct shoulder stripe and the legs show bars up to the knees.

Semi-wild horses

Horses readily go feral. This has happened in so many places that it helps us to understand how easily the wild horses surviving after domestication should have become diluted by crossing with domestic stock. Well known examples are the half-wild mustangs of the United States and the brumbies of Australia. In Britain the New Forest, Exmoor and Dartmoor ponies are probably in the same class but have been semi-wild for so long that their ancestry is open to argument.

Smiling with anger

Wild horses live in large herds on steppes and grassy plains. A herd consists of mares, foals and colts led by a stallion. As the male colts reach maturity they are driven to the fringes of the herd by the boss stallion. Feral and domestic horses tend towards the same formations but in smaller numbers. Being herd animals they have the usual need for communication between individuals by the use of facial expression and posture. Aggression is shown by laying the ears back and opening the mouth to show the teeth, the corners of the mouth being drawn up. Friendliness or greeting is similar but with the ears erect and the corners of the mouth not drawn up although the mouth is open to show the teeth. Appeasement or submissiveness, as when a young stallion approaches the boss stallion without intent to challenge his authority, is shown by holding the head low with the ears depressed sideways to almost the horizontal and opening the mouth, this time to make nibbling movements with the front teeth. A more marked sign of friendliness is to nibble the skin of the dominant individual near the root of his tail. This is enough to turn hostility to harmony and the dominant will tend thereafter to present his hindquarters for the tail root to be nibbled. A mare in season also shows her teeth to the stallion but with ears erect. At the same time she raises her hindquarters and turns her tail to one side.

Fighting between stallions is with the hoofs of the forefeet, the contestants rear-

ing up on hindlegs to do so. At a later stage the teeth are used for savage biting, especially at the neck. For defence against natural enemies, such as wolves, kicking with the hindhoofs is probably the first line of defence when a single individual is attacked. Since feral horses sometimes form into a line abreast, when alarmed, we may suppose this represents the formation of a phalanx to protect the herd as a whole, and especially as a screen to protect the young.

The foal is born about 11 months after mating. A young male is called a colt until 4 years old, while a female is called a filly until that age. Horses commonly live to 20 years; ages of 30—40 years are not infrequent, the record being 62.

Horses in battle

Domestication of the horse has made a tremendous impact on the history of mankind. From the many antiquities on which the horse is portrayed it seems that horses were first used for chariots, more than for single riders. In time, however, they were used as pack animals, for heavier transport—and especially for cavalry. The tendency has always been for the best horses to be reserved for monarchs and the nobility. They were, and still are, a status symbol. In the Near East, especially, a horse meant everything to its rider, valued as highly as, or even more highly than, his own children. In war, the conquests of Genghis Khan and of the Mohammedans would have been impossible without horses. The latter swept across North Africa and up through Spain. They were stopped at Poitiers in 732 AD when they met the Franks, who were mounted on heavier horses. The mounted horsemen of the Spanish *conquistadores* were decisive in the conquest of South America. In North America the aboriginal Indians quickly learned to use the horse, while the pioneers were dependent on it not only to fight the Indians but to round up cattle.

Domestic breeds

The monarch of the horse world is the Arab, a lightly built and delicate breed noted for its bulging forehead and concave profile, slender muzzle, arched neck, short and straight back and long graceful legs. As with almost everything else connected with the history of horses it is a matter for argument how the Arab and the other breeds came into being. It seems likely there were several subspecies of wild horse across Europe and Asia and that the earliest breeds of domesticated horses reflect the differences between them. It is possible also that domestication arose independently in different places. What seems certain is that there were eventually the Arabs and the northern horses.

The latter were mainly of two types, a heavy horse and a lighter Celtic horse, of which the Iceland pony is a typical form. In the last thousand years or so, and increasingly as time went on, Arab stallions were imported into Europe to improve the strains of other breeds.

In time the heavy northern horses came to carry the heavily-armoured knights of the age of chivalry. When armour went out of fashion the heavy cavalry persisted but the breeds became more especially diverted to menial tasks, drawing heavy wagons and drays. Yet the horses retained their magnificence in the shire, Clydesdale and Suffolk, in the Belgian as well as in the Percheron, a somewhat lighter breed. Others of the 60 or so breeds are the Hackney, the high-stepping horse of the days of carriages, before the internal combustion engine; the Welsh pony and, at the opposite end of the scale from the shire and the Clydesdale, the Shetland pony. A famous breed on the other side of the Atlantic is the Morgan horse which sprang from a single progenitor. In

Sunset scene in the Camargue, southern France, a region famous for its herds of semi-wild horses. After a roundup, a group of them is herded along the skyline under the watchful eye of one of the skilled herdsmen.

1795 a small bay stallion was foaled in Vermont which sired a breed named after its owner Justin Morgan. The breed became the favourite carriage horse in the United States and was used also as a cavalry and police mount. It probably had thoroughbred blood but was heavier than the thoroughbred, the breed with Arab blood, famous in horse racing.

Horse evolution

In 1838 William Colchester, a brickmaker of Kingston in Suffolk, was digging out clay for bricks when he unearthed a fossil tooth. The next year, at Studd Hill in Kent, William Richardson was collecting fossils when he found what looked like the skull of a hare. As time passed more fossils of this kind were found of an animal to which the name *Hyracotherium* was given. It has also been called *Eohippus*, the 'dawn-horse' which lived 70 million years ago. Although its teeth are not like those of a horse the skull is, but its forefeet had four toes and the hindfeet had three. During the century following those first two discoveries in England many fossils have been dug out of the ground and put together. When arranged in a chronological series they give us an almost complete picture of the geological history of horses. As we pass along the row

we see the animal growing in size. At the same time the skull twists slightly on its long axis to turn it from what seems to be almost a hare's skull to the heavy skull of the modern horse. The cheek teeth at first are small with cusps, not unlike our own molars, and these gradually change to the grinding teeth of the modern horse, with ridges on the upper surface, well suited to grinding grasses, the basic food of present-day horses. And while these changes are going on the legs are getting longer and one by one the toes are dwindling in size and dropping out altogether, except for the middle toe bones which are growing longer and stouter. In the end, in the modern horse, the bones of the lower leg are made up of the bones of the middle toe with the nail enormously enlarged to form a hoof.

There are few animals for which we have so complete a series of ancestral bones. Yet there are those, especially people fond of horses, who find it hard to accept the idea that this noble beast started as an animal the size of a hare. If we stretch a point and say that man has been selectively breeding horses for 3 500 years we find he has managed to produce such contrasts as the Shetland pony at most 42 in. high—Shetlands are always measured in inches—and the shire horse 17 hands high—a hand is 4 in.—capable of pulling a load of 5 tons. The

changes from *Hyracotherium* to the wild horse are somewhat greater, it is true, but the time during which they took place is 20 thousand times longer than the 3½ thousand years needed to produce the Shetland and the Clydesdale.

class	**Mammalia**
order	**Perissodactyla**
family	**Equidae**
genus & species	***Equus caballus*** *E. caballus gmelini* tarpan *E. caballus przewalskii* *Przewalski's horse*

▷ *Pastureland violence: a pair of horses locked in foot and tooth combat. This is probably a minor dominance battle, with few injuries; fights between wild horses are usually much more vicious. Horses have a variety of expressions and postures to show their feelings towards one another; ears back and mouth open with the corners drawn up means aggression; ears erect and mouth open without curling means friendship, and submissiveness is shown by drooping ears and nibbling movements of the lips.*
▽ *Wet stampede: a herd of Camargue horses shatters the calm of a shallow stream.*

We-Ha

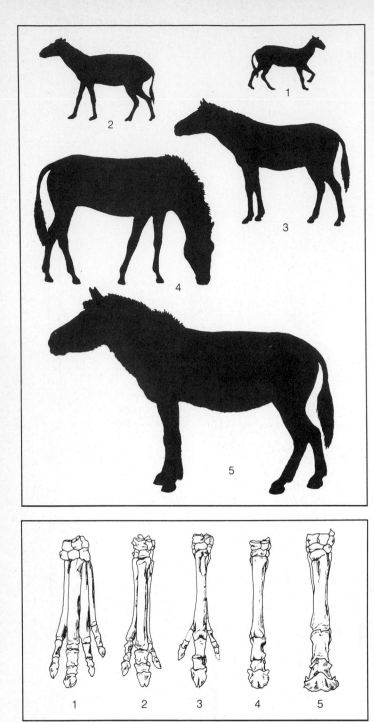

A classic chain of evolution

*Fifty million years ago the ancestor of the modern horse was a little hare-like animal **Eohippus** (1) running in the swampy undergrowth on four long, splayed toes. As times became drier and great plains developed the descendants of this 'dawn horse' evolved longer legs, better adapted for running from predators in their new open environment. In 20 million years one toe was lost as in **Mesohippus** (2). During the next 20 million years the two outer toes were much reduced as in **Merychippus** (3) probably only touching the ground in wetter patches. **Pliohippus** (4) which lived in the Pliocene period 10−1 million years ago, ran on only one long toe and the modern horse **Equus** (5) has reached the extreme — running on its toe nail, the hoof. (Horse outlines to scale, respective toes not to scale.) Top: Przewalski's horse, a wild horse discovered in Central Asia in 1881. Top centre: Shaggy-coated Shetland pony, one of the smallest of modern horses. Bottom centre: the other end of the scale, a shire stallion, a massive horse capable of pulling a load of 5 tons. Right: the peak of selective breeding, a thoroughbred racehorse, descended from Arab stock*

*Beauty in life: the face of a deerfly **Chrysops coecutiens**. The brilliant colours fade after death, and are lost in preserved specimens.*

Horsefly

This name is given to certain large flies belonging to the genus **Tabanus.** The females feed on the blood of animals, especially horses and cattle, the males on nectar from flowers. The name horsefly is often used to describe all the flies of the family Tabanidae, all of which feed in the same way. Among them are the well-known flies called 'clegs' which greatly relish human blood and can be a serious nuisance in warm weather on moors and in woodland. The deer flies **Chrysops** also belong to the Tabanidae. The true horseflies are sometimes called 'stouts', probably on account of their size; the largest British species **Tabanus sudeticus** may be an inch long and have a wing span of nearly 2 in. Horseflies and clegs are dull grey or brown with clear or mottled wings, but the equally bloodthirsty deer flies are handsome insects, brown and yellow, the wings clear with distinct brown markings. In many tabanids the eyes are wonderfully beautiful, with rainbow-like bands of gold, red and green. Unfortunately these colours fade after death and are not seen in preserved specimens.

Horseflies are not important as carriers of disease, but are nevertheless very harmful to cattle, causing disturbance and loss of grazing time, and consequent deterioration in health. In some parts of the world herdsmen drive their cattle out to graze through the summer night and keep them in shelter by day, simply to protect them from horseflies.

horsefly makes quite a big hole, and when the fly withdraws its mouthparts a drop of blood oozes out. It feeds both by licking up the drop and by sucking from the wound. It has been estimated that a single grazing beast may lose as much as 100 cu cm of blood in this way in the course of a summer day.

Our knowledge of horseflies' habits is based mainly on females that come to bite. Males are seldom seen and are comparatively rare in entomological collections. They are known to feed on nectar from flowers but are seldom observed doing so.

In the tropical rain forest of Uganda some of the commonest flies of the forest floor are biting horseflies, but for a long time only females were known. Then, as part of a programme of entomological research, scaffolding and platforms were put up, so scientists could go up and watch near the treetops or jungle canopy. In and above this hitherto inaccessible environment were found swarms of male horseflies, together with occasional females. Presumably these females fly up to find a mate and then descend again to resume their quest for blood. Another curious habit of male horseflies is darting down to take water from lakes and streams in the same way as swifts and swallows do.

Cannibalistic larvae

Although about 3 000 species of horseflies, in the broader sense, are known (28 in Britain) we know very little about their life histories. Such larvae that are known live in shallow water, in mud and sand by streams or in damp soil. They are elongate creatures with rather leathery skins and a breathing tube or siphon at the tip of the abdomen. Those of the big *Tabanus* horseflies are carnivorous and will eat any other insects, worms, snails, tadpoles and even each other! A number kept together in one container is soon reduced to one well-fed larva. They catch their prey with a pair of strong, curved, vertically moving jaws. The larvae of the pretty marble-winged deerflies live on vegetable rubbish and can easily be reared in numbers in a shallow-water aquarium. All horsefly larvae tend to seek drier surroundings to pupate; even aquatic larvae leave the water and pupate in mud or damp soil.

Once seen . . .

An insect collector in Africa once came upon a swarm of horseflies of both sexes, evidently just emerging from their pupae. He collected a large number, and they proved to be a new species. He was generous in distributing his specimens and the species is now well represented in collections—but it has never been seen alive since by the collector or anyone else!

phylum	**Arthropoda**
class	**Insecta**
order	**Diptera**
family	**Tabanidae**
genera	**Tabanus, Haematopota** clegs **Chrysops** deerflies

Carlo Bevilacqua

*The real menace: most people are shy of wasps and hornets, but once in damp pasture horseflies are the most painful and persistent of biters. Above: **Tabanus bromius** takes a rest. Left: The piercing mouthparts of a deerfly.*

Constance P Warner

Bloodthirsty females

Horseflies may sometimes be seen sitting and sunning themselves on tree trunks and fence posts, but are far more often seen feeding on cattle or horses, or flying around them. The clegs and other smaller tabanids may often be discovered on the clothing or exposed skin of a companion on a walk, or located on oneself by the sharp, painful prick that accompanies their bite. The big horseflies fly with quite a loud hum, but clegs and deerflies arrive silently on the victim's coat collar or sleeve and then stealthily make their way to the nearest area of exposed skin. They are not very quick and wary and one can usually swat a cleg that has bitten, but where they occur they are numerous, and are in no way deterred by casualties among their fellows.

Tabanid flies have sharp, blade-like mandibles and maxillae and use these to pierce the skin of their victims. The bite of a large

Horsehair worm

The adults of these long thin worms, which as larvae are parasites in insects, are sometimes found in freshwater. From 4 to 40 in. long but only $\frac{1}{80} - \frac{1}{8}$ in. across, they were once thought in the Middle Ages to be born of horsehairs that had fallen into water. An alternative name is 'hair worms', their thread-like form being reflected also in their scientific name Nematomorpha. The way they become entangled in masses of 2 – 20 worms has earned them the names of 'gordian worms' or Gordioidea, a reference to the knot tied by Gordius and cut by Alexander the Great.

The adults of a given species vary considerably in length and in colour from yellowish to almost black. The males of some species end at the back in two lobes while those of other species are simply rounded at the hind end like the majority of females. (The hind end of the female Paragordius is three-lobed.) Females are generally longer than males. Enclosing the unsegmented body is a tough cuticle covered, according to the species, with a variety of tiny furrows, warts, spines and other ornaments.

Horsehair worms are related to the much more important nematode worms which include eelworms and roundworms, and are easily confused with another kind, the mermithid nematodes which are also parasites of insects but taper at each end. There are about 80 species of horsehair worm of which four are found in Britain. All but one belong to the order Gordioidea, but there is a single marine species Nectonema that is parasitic in its young stages in crabs and which is classified separately.

Gordian knots are marriage knots

Adult horsehair worms live in temperate and tropical regions in all kinds of freshwater; mountain streams, temporary pools, damp earth, marshes, underground waters, even in dogs' drinking bowls. The females are sluggish and move little, the males swim clumsily by undulating the body by contractions of longitudinally-arranged muscles. They have no circular muscles to give ease and grace to their swimming. The adults do not feed, their digestive tract being degenerate and apparently functionless. Usually they have no mouth, but this means little because food is not swallowed at any time during the life history. In the parasitic stage it is absorbed through the general body surfaces.

The entangled 'Gordian knots' contain mating pairs. The male coils the hind part of his body around that of the female and deposits sperm near her cloacal opening. These migrate into a sperm receptacle where they are stored for a few days until the time of egg laying. The eggs are laid in long, gelatinous strings, a fraction of an inch to more than 1 in. long, which swell on contact with water to produce masses often

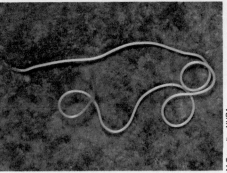

Gordius villoti — a gordian worm.

larger than the parent worm. These masses, often attached to stones or weed, may contain several million eggs $\frac{1}{500}$ in. diameter. Like so many parasites, the horsehair worms lay prodigious numbers of eggs to ensure the survival of the species. The males die after mating and the females after laying their eggs.

Driving insects to drink

The eggs hatch in 3 – 11 weeks according to the temperature. The larvae are unlike the adults. Their cylindrical ringed bodies are about $\frac{1}{125}$ in. long and divided into a trunk and, at the front, a shorter muscular region from which they can shoot out a proboscis bearing three circlets of hooks and three long stylets.

Soon after hatching, the larva may encyst on vegetation near the water's edge. Within its cyst, it can survive for several months, even if the water level falls and it dries out. Indeed, exposure by falling water level actually helps infection of the host. The cyst or the free larva may be eaten by an insect or millipede along with the vegetation on which it is lying. The cyst wall then breaks down and the released larva bores through the intestinal wall of the host and into its body. Here the larva gradually

digests the surrounding tissues and absorbs them through its surface. Eventually it metamorphoses and develops in a few weeks or months into a long adult, tightly coiled —perhaps with others—in the host's body cavity. If the host insect becomes wetted or falls into water, the mature worm breaks out through the body wall, usually near the anus. Not all adult worms then find themselves in a suitable body of water and so do not live to reproduce. Perhaps the presence of mature gordians in the host insects somehow influences them to seek water.

Harmless to man

The insects normally parasitised by horsehair worms include a wide range of beetles, grasshoppers, crickets and cockroaches, but gordians have also been seen coming out of caddisflies and dragonflies. Different species of horsehair worms probably vary in the range of insects they parasitise. Many larvae are eaten by abnormal hosts such as the larvae of mayflies and stoneflies, but in these they either die or re-encyst in the tissues. In the latter case, the worms may still grow to maturity provided the abnormal host is eaten by a more suitable carnivorous or omnivorous insect. For example, the giant water beetle *Dytiscus* has been known to become infected by eating tadpoles. On rare occasions the larvae turn up in odd places, in a fluke, the intestinal wall of a fish and the faeces of a child who had perhaps swallowed it in ill-chosen drinking water. Sometimes the presence of horsehair worms in water supplies causes great alarm and in some regions there is a belief that cows die soon after swallowing such animals. Horsehair worms are, however, almost entirely harmless to mammals, and the curious case of an adult specimen of *Paragordius* living in the urinary passages of a girl is not only difficult to explain but quite exceptional.

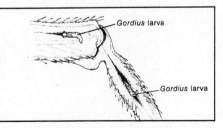

phylum	**Aschelminthes**
class	**Nematomorpha**
order	**Gordioidea**
genera	***Gordius, Paragordius***
order	**Nectonematoidea**
genus	***Nectonema***

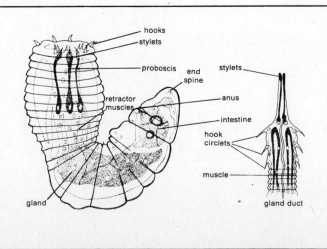

*Gordius larvae in the leg of an insect (top left). It is thought that the stylets penetrate the body wall of the host, probably by boring. These hooks and stylets are clearly seen (left) on the extended proboscis of **Paragordius**, and in the larva (far left). The cylindrical body of the larva is ringed and divided into a trunk and a shorter muscular region from which the proboscis is protruded.*

hooks
stylets
proboscis
end spine
stylets
retractor muscles
anus
intestine
hook circlets
muscle
gland
gland duct

1089

Horseshoe bat

The horseshoe bats belong to the Microchiroptera but are readily distinguished from others of this suborder by their nose-leaves. This is the name given to the folds of skin on the faces of many bats. In the horseshoe bats the pattern of the nose-leaves includes one part shaped like a horseshoe. This covers the upper lip and surrounds the nostrils. Above it is a narrow pointed flap of skin, known as the lancet. Horseshoe bats differ markedly from other bats in many features of their behaviour, and especially in the way they use echolocation.

Their ears are large and are without an earlet (tragus). Their eyes are small and their field of vision obstructed by the large nose-leaf, so sight probably plays little part in their lives. The females, which are slightly smaller than the males, have two dummy teats on the abdomen as well as the functional teats on the chest, the dummy teats being used by the baby to hang on to the mother when being carried in flight.

There are 50 species of horseshoe bats in temperate and tropical regions of the Old World, all similar in appearance and behaviour. The two European species are typical of the rest.

The greater horseshoe bat has a 2¾in. head and body with a 1½in. tail and a wingspan of up to 15 in. The weight varies throughout the year, being heaviest in December when the male weighs up to ¾ oz and the female weighs ⅝ oz. The ears are large, ½ in. long ending in a sharp tip. The fur is thick and woolly and ash-grey on the back and covers both surfaces of the wing membrane for a short way. The fur of the underside has a yellowish or pinkish tinge.

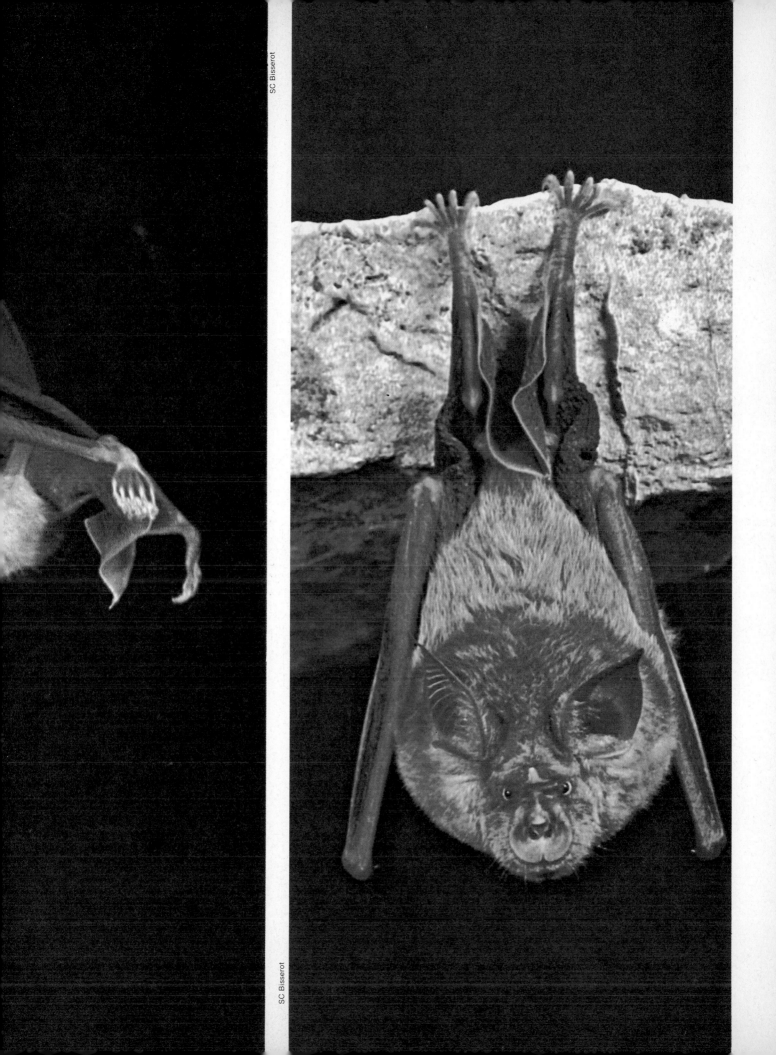

Late risers

The horseshoe bat comes out from its roost rather late in the evening; it returns to roost and flies out again several times during the night. It flies low on the wing, sometimes only a few inches off the ground and at most 10 ft high. Its flight is heavy and butterfly-like, with frequent glides. By day, in summer, it sleeps in caves, tunnels, dark buildings, lofts and roof spaces, sometimes in hollow trees, usually in colonies but occasionally singly. Males and females occupy separate roosts.

Hibernation

Hibernation, which lasts from October to the end of March, is usually in caves and tunnels. It may sometimes begin in September or be continued until May or June, depending on the weather. It is not as continuous as was formerly supposed. There is much movement in the caves, the bats moving about and some flying from one cave to another as much as 40 miles apart. Movement is influenced by temperature. Normally horseshoe bats sleep singly, in clusters of half-dozens or in larger clusters, typically hanging by the toes of the hindfeet from the ceiling of the cave and with the wings wrapped around the body like a cloak. Should the temperature drop they may cluster more for warmth, each bat holding its wing out to absorb extra heat. They will also move to another part of the cave when the temperature drops below 6°C/42°F, seeking spots where it is up to 8°C/46°F.

Even in a cave hibernating horseshoe bats sense when the temperature outside rises to 10°C/50°F. They will then come out to feed on dung beetles which seem to be active during winter, returning if the temperature falls. Further proof that the hibernation is intermittent is seen in the accumulations of bat guano on the floor of the caves during each winter and the fact that the bats themselves gain weight. The females lose weight rapidly until February then gain weight. The males remain steady until mid-December, when their weight drops sharply but increases in the last month of hibernation.

Feeding on the ground

Horseshoe bats feed more especially on beetles and moths. They have been seen to settle on the ground or on stems of grass to take ground-living beetles. They also eat spiders. Small insects taken on the wing are devoured straight away, the larger ones are carried to a resting place to be eaten there. The bats cannot walk on a flat surface and to alight they turn a somersault in the air to land by the feet, head downwards.

Hanging up the baby

Mating is promiscuous, between October and mid-December but the sperms lie quiescent in the female's reproductive tract until the spring. Then, after a gestation of 6 weeks, the young are born in June and July. The single baby is hairless and blind, and its wings are pale coloured. At first the mother takes her baby with her when hunting. It clings to her fur with its claws and holds one of the false nipples in its mouth. Later she hangs it up in the roost when she goes out foraging. Newly born bats have relatively large heads, ears and feet. They also have the instinct to climb upwards, but should one fall to the ground it dies from inhaling the strong ammonia from the guano. Horseshoe bats mature at 3 years, and are known to live at least 17½ years.

Scientists' snap

In 1938 a young graduate at Harvard University, Donald R Griffin, became interested in ultrasonics and in the next few years had unravelled the story of how bats use echolocation to find their way about and to find their prey. Meanwhile war had broken out in Europe and for the next six years Germany was cut off from the rest of the world as regards the exchange of scientific information. During those years Franz Mohres in Germany was discovering the same story as Griffin. Not until the war had ended and exchange of scientific knowledge had been resumed was it possible to know that two men on opposite sides of the Atlantic had been doing the same work.

Griffin's discovery was made on vesper bats which fly with the mouth open emitting squeaks through it in regular short pulses.

J Hooper

The echoes from these, bouncing off solid objects, are picked up by the ears giving the bats a sound-picture of their surroundings. Mohres worked on horseshoe bats which fly with the mouth shut, sending out squeaks through the nostrils. They send out 'explosive' pulses at more infrequent intervals and the horseshoe-shaped nose-leaf forms a movable cup by which the pulses can be beamed. This is best illustrated by the way a horseshoe bat, hanging by its feet, can twist itself on its hips through almost a complete circle scanning the air around, often darting off suddenly to seize an insect that flies within range.

class	**Mammalia**
order	**Chiroptera**
suborder	**Microchiroptera**
family	**Rhinolophidae**
genus & species	***Rhinolophus ferrumequinum*** *greater horseshoe bat* ***R. hipposideros*** *lesser horseshoe bat others*

The greater horseshoe bat (left and previous pages) and also the lesser horseshoe bat are easily recognisable by their characteristic nose-leaves. These expansions of the skin consist of a lower part shaped like a horseshoe surrounding the upper lip and nostrils, and an upper part, the lancet, a narrow pointed flap of skin. It is thought the nose-leaves may direct the sounds emitted through the nostrils. These bats roost where they are able to hang freely (below). Unlike most bats that close their wings alongside their bodies the horseshoe bats wrap their wings around their bodies so they are completely enclosed in their flight membranes, looking very much like fruit pods.

SC Bisserot

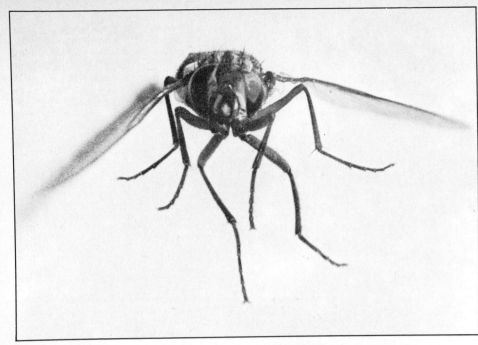

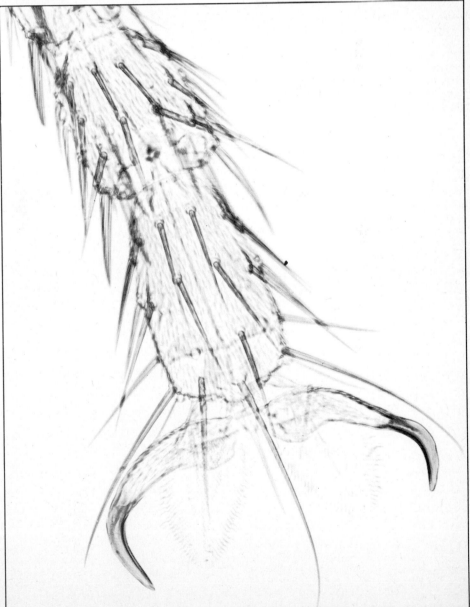

B Leidmann: Bavara

△ *Wings of housefly (top) and lesser housefly (bottom). The differences in venation can be used to distinguish the two types of fly.*
◁ *Housefly with legs askew just about to land.*
▽ *Photomicrograph of a leg. The last segment has a pair of claws and two suction pads which help the fly to walk on smooth surfaces (× 60).*

Housefly

Many different kinds of flies come into houses. Some are accidental intruders that buzz on the window panes trying to get out into the open air again. Others enter houses in the autumn to hibernate in attics and roof-spaces. But there are two kinds that make our houses their home. One is the housefly, the other is the lesser housefly. The first is stoutly built and in both sexes the abdomen is yellowish or buff. Lesser houseflies are smaller and more slender, the females dull greyish, the males similar but with a pair of semi-transparent yellow patches at the base of the abdomen. The two are also distinguished by a difference in the veins of the wings which can easily be seen with a lens. This difference separates the two species regardless of sex.

Both have a wide distribution, the housefly being found throughout the tropics as well as in almost all inhabited temperate regions.

Kiss-in-the-ring flight

Houseflies pass their adult lives in houses, flying about the rooms and crawling over food that is left exposed. Both species breed in the sort of refuse that accumulates around the dwellings of people who live unhygienically, but their habits differ in detail. Lesser houseflies appear earlier in the season than houseflies, which build up their numbers rather slowly after the winter and are not usually abundant until July. The males of lesser houseflies fly in a very distinctive way. They choose a spot in a room, often beneath a hanging lamp or similar 'landmark', and fly as if they were following the sides of a triangle or quadrilateral, hovering momentarily at the corners and turning sharply at them; a single fly will continue to follow the same course for long periods. If, as often happens, more

Barnabys

A housefly cleans itself by rubbing its first pair of legs together. This common fly spreads disease mainly as a result of its indiscriminate feeding habits. Bacteria may be carried on the legs or body, or in the proboscis and so be exuded onto food with the next flow of saliva.

than one fly is patrolling in the same area, one of them will intercept the other and the two whirl together for an instant and then part again. The expression 'playing kiss-in-the-ring' aptly describes this activity, but they are in fact all males, and always lesser houseflies.

Flies in summer — and winter

The breeding habits of the two species are similar but the larva of the lesser housefly prefers food rich in nitrogenous compounds, such as urine or bird droppings. These flies are nearly always abundant where chickens are kept. The larvae of the housefly are less particular. Manure and compost heaps, the night soil from old-fashioned privies and house refuse of any kind all provide them with breeding-grounds.

The eggs are laid on the larval food, and the adult flies also feed in places of this kind. The eggs are white, about $\frac{1}{25}$ in. long and a female housefly may lay as many as 900 in batches of about 150. They hatch in as little as 8 hours if it is very warm, otherwise in 1 — 3 days. The white legless maggots feed rapidly and may reach full size in under 2 days, but can live for 8 weeks in colder and less favourable conditions. At 15°C/60°F houseflies will breed continuously throughout the year, taking about 3 weeks from egg to adult, but in the tropics the cycle is completed in a week. The pupa is formed in an oval brown capsule called the puparium, which consists of the last larval skin; instead of being shed at pupation this is retained and plays the same part as the moth cocoon.

The lesser housefly has a similar life cycle, but its larva is very different in appearance, being flattened and beset with rows of short branched tentacle-like processes on the upper surface of the body.

Flies disappear in winter time, and the question where they go is often asked — and it once formed the theme of a popular song. There seems no simple answer to it. Houseflies may hibernate as adults or continue breeding slowly in warm places, especially in buildings where cattle are kept. Probably

the fly has different adaptations for wintering in different parts of its range. In warm regions it breeds all the year round.

Sucking up their food

Adults of both species feed by settling on moist organic matter of almost any kind and sucking up nutrient liquid from it. If the material is dry the fly regurgitates a drop of liquid onto it and sucks up the resultant solution. Crude sewage and a bowl of sugar are equally attractive and the insect may fly straight from one to the other. The feeding apparatus consists of a short sucking proboscis expanded at the end into a sponge-like organ with which the fly mops up its liquid food. Flies that have overfilled their stomachs will often regurgitate on any surface on which they happen to be resting, leaving little dirty spots.

People will sometimes assure you that they have been bitten by a housefly. The mistake is excusable because the stable fly *Stomoxys calcitrans* looks almost exactly like a housefly. Its mouthparts are, however, very different, consisting of a stiff piercing organ, and they feed, as horseflies do, by sucking blood. Their bite is quite painful and they can penetrate one's skin through a thick sock. The stable fly breeds in dung mixed with straw and is far less common now than when horses were kept in large numbers.

Bearers of disease

The most important disease-carrying insects are those which feed on our blood, taking micro-organisms from infected people and injecting them into the blood of healthy ones. Examples are the tsetse fly and some mosquitoes. Houseflies do not feed in this way, but by feeding on excrement and exposed foodstuffs they are potential carriers of gastro-intestinal diseases such as dysentery. Houseflies taken from a slum district have been found to carry on average over $3\frac{1}{2}$ million bacteria per fly, and over a million in clean districts. These are not all disease bacteria, but some of them are very likely to be. Infants and small children seem to

suffer most from fly-borne disease. In a tropical village infant mortality dropped in one year from 22·7 to 11·5 per cent when flies were controlled by an insecticide.

It is not difficult to kill flies in vast numbers by spraying such substances as DDT and chlordane on the places where they feed and breed but they have a remarkable capacity for developing resistance to specific poisons. No individual fly develops resistance during its lifetime, but some will almost always survive a spraying and these will include individuals having, by an accident of nature, some degree of immunity to the pesticide being used. This immunity is inherited by their offspring, in varying degrees, and the most resistant of these will again survive and breed. Selection of this kind continues with every generation until the insecticide is useless in any concentration at which it is safe to use. The process is exactly the same as the natural selection through which evolution has taken its course. These examples of acquired resistance in insects are in fact examples of very rapid evolutionary change, and they form one of the most compelling arguments against relying too much upon pesticides in our efforts to control harmful insects.

Control of houseflies is best achieved by depriving them of breeding places. The modern civilised way of life has already gone a long way towards doing this. Water-borne sanitation, the use of covered dustbins and the decline of the horse as a means of transport are three obvious factors, but flies will be with us for a long time yet, especially in regions with hot climates. We must still wage war on them by the best means available and try to exclude them from our houses and, above all, keep them away from our food.

class	**Insecta**
order	**Diptera**
family	**Muscidae**
genera & species	***Musca domestica*** *housefly* ***Fannia canicularis*** *lesser housefly*

House mouse

This is probably the most familiar and the most widely distributed rodent. Although often found in woods and fields it lives mainly in or around buildings especially where food is stored—even in large meat refrigerators, in constant darkness and with temperatures below freezing point.

The house mouse has a 3—4in. head and body length and weighs $\frac{1}{4}$—$1\frac{1}{3}$ oz. It has a scale-ringed, sparsely-haired tail about the same length as the body, a pointed muzzle and moderately large ears and eyes. Its fur is brownish grey, slightly paler on the underparts.

It used to be thought that the house mouse, like the common and ship rats, originated in Central Asia. The present view is that its original range probably included the Mediterranean area, both southern Europe and North Africa, and most of the steppe zone of Asia as far east as Japan. Certainly it was known in Europe at the time of Ancient Greece, but it has now spread all over the world, largely through being accidentally carried by man. It is now found wherever there are human habitations, in the Tropics as well as in the Arctic. At first mice were taken from country to country across the seas by ship. Today stowaways go by air as well.

▷ A house mouse grooming. This small rodent has a long tail, the same length as its body, that is scale-ringed and sparsely-haired.
▽ Making sure all is clear before leaving.

Swift and silent mover

Mainly but not wholly nocturnal, the house mouse moves quickly and silently. It can also climb well up walls of brick or concrete. When suddenly alarmed, it can leap surprising distances, especially over vertical barriers, and it can squeeze through holes as small as ⅜ in. diameter. Throughout its present range it has become mainly associated with man but not merely in towns. House mice have been found in isolated buildings well away from towns and villages even in the Tropics. They are usually found in buildings in warmer countries but this may be because they are killed off by predators in open country. On islands where predators are virtually non-existent mice have become established in the countryside away from buildings.

Wild origins

According to the experts there were originally four wild subspecies. One of these, the original outdoor form, is small with the tail considerably shorter than the head and body length. The other three which became commensal with man have since given rise to numerous other subspecies. Even these have become thoroughly mixed by interbreeding, with a resulting wide range of colour varieties, dark and light as well as the typical mouse grey. Sometimes these indoor mice will live out of doors but, as a rule, only where there are cultivated crops. There are also the strains of tame and laboratory mice and breeds that are hairless except for the whiskers. One example of how strains of wild house mice can differ is seen in the ease with which mice in country houses can be trapped as compared with the difficulty of trapping those living in London.

The dreaded mousy smell

House mice have territories which they mark with their urine, and this is responsible for the 'mousy smell' from mice kept in captivity. This leads to people cleaning out their cages, but it has been found in animal rooms attached to laboratories that the more the mice cages are cleaned out the more energetically do the occupants mark their cages with urine until the odour from them becomes unbearable. Individuals occupying a territory can be recognized by each other by their odour. Experiments have shown that a 'foreign' mouse introduced into a territory after having been artificially supplied with the odour from those living in the territory is readily accepted by them. Otherwise a 'foreign' mouse wandering into the territory is driven out. The aggressive attitude of the house mouse is to rear up on the hindlegs and hold the forepaws together, with the nose in the air. It looks almost an attitude of prayer, and it can occasionally be seen when a cat is playing with a mouse. The cat drops the mouse, which turns to face the cat as if pleading for mercy. It is, in fact, showing fight — usually with a notable lack of success.

Myopic mice

The senses of smell and hearing are the two most important to house mice. It is commonplace for those writing about small mammals generally, and mice in particular, to speak of their bright beady eyes, implying keen sight. In fact, mice are myopic. It is doubtful whether in daylight they see much beyond a range of 2 in., although how their eyes serve them at night has not been fully studied.

Dominant males

The social structure of the mouse colony is loose until the population builds up to overcrowding. Then a social hierarchy is formed with one male dominant over the rest, and he alone mates with the females. It provides a natural brake to further overcrowding. Nevertheless there are frequent instances, notably in California and Australia, of mouse plagues, when the ground is alive with them in their tens of thousands in quite small areas.

Surviving on flour

House mice are basically seed and grain eaters but they readily adapt to a wide variety of other foods. Those living permanently in the meat cold stores eat meat only. They are larger and heavier than usual, have longer coats and make their nests in the carcases. During the Second World War 'buffer depots' of flour were set up in Britain. Mice invading these were able to live on flour alone and with very little water. House mice that have lived on household wastes and in larders seem unable to revert to natural foods, as shown by the St Kilda mice, which soon died out when the human inhabitants left the island in 1930.

Five litters a year

The success of the house mouse owes as much to its breeding rate as to its adaptability in feeding and finding shelter in buildings. They breed through most of the year. In houses they average just over five litters a year with an average of five to a litter. In cold stores the averages are six litters a year and six to a litter. In grain stores they average 8–10 litters a year. Gestation is 19–20 days, and the young are born blind and naked. They are weaned at 18 days and at the age of 6 weeks begin to breed. The life-span is up to 3 years, although house mice have been kept in captivity for 6 years.

Driven out of home

Mice living outdoors have many enemies. They include the obvious examples of birds and beasts of prey such as hawks and owls, weasels, stoats, foxes and cats, and also the occasional omnivores, such as crows and rats, all of which normally take small animals. Where mice abound, snakes often make them their staple diet. There is a rooted belief in some quarters that rats and mice cannot live together, that if you have mice in a house there will be no rats. It is more likely that when rats take up residence they kill off the mice. Where close studies have been made it has been found that the house mouse cannot compete successfully even with the long-tailed fieldmouse which, although about the same size, is the more active. It is even suggested that the long-tail drives out or kills the house mouse. This can only happen in the wild because the long-tail rarely enters buildings, so there are no encounters.

The dancing mice

One of the famous breeds of house mouse is the waltzing mouse of Japan, a freak breed which runs around in circles. There are also singing mice. These can be heard at a distance of 20 yd literally singing like a bird. This is because they have a diseased larynx or diseased lungs. Another seemingly artistic mouse was the one recorded by the Rev JG Woods, a famous naturalist of the mid-19th century. In his *Natural History* dated 1852 he made the statement that the house mouse 'is said to be greatly susceptible of music'. To support this he told of 'a gentleman who was playing a violin seeing a mouse run along the floor and jump about as if distracted. He continued the strain, and after some time the mouse, apparently exhausted with its exertions, dropped dead on the floor'.

One recent discovery is that house mice and many other small rodents, use ultrasonics. Some of their squeaks can be heard by the human ear but others are too high-pitched. A baby mouse will call in ultrasonics, for example, when its mother sits heavily on it. A mouse's ears are sensitive to high-pitched sounds, which we cannot hear. If you rub your finger round and round over the glass of a cage in which a mouse is confined you see the mouse's ears moving in time with your finger. Then, as the operation goes on, the mouse begins to get restless and in the end it is running and bounding as if in a frenzy (or as if it were dancing to music). The rattling of a bunch of keys near a mouse may have the same effect. There has been a great deal of research on this as a result of which we speak of mice suffering from audiogenic seizures. Not all house mice are affected by this, but in others the audiogenic seizure may be fatal. This, beyond doubt, is the explanation of the story told by the Rev JG Woods, and it is of interest his story, frowned upon for a century, should have received support from modern research.

class	**Mammalia**
order	**Rodentia**
family	**Muridae**
genus & species	***Mus musculus***

▷ *A pretty pair of house mice sitting peacefully at home in a barn. There are commensal and wild forms of this common mouse, the scourge of many housewives. Both have brownish grey fur that is slightly lighter on the underparts, large ears and eyes and a pointed muzzle. Although the eyes look bright and keen these mice are in fact short-sighted and rely on their senses of smell and hearing. The commensal forms often move out from buildings in the spring and summer and return in the autumn for shelter. They will feed on any human food that is available damaging much more than they eat and seeming to survive on very little, hence the saying 'poor as a church mouse'. The wild forms eat mainly vegetables, such as seeds, roots, leaves and stems. These small mammals, pests in the house, are of great importance in research. The albino strains in particular are used in laboratory work.*

A house shrew surrounded by its meal of kitchen refuse. This shrew originally lived in the forests of India but has taken to living in houses and has been accidentally introduced to other countries.

Jane Burton: Photo Res

House shrew

The house shrew, or musk rat as it is sometimes called, is one of about 20 species, belonging to a genus that contains some of the largest shrews and one of the smallest mammals, the dwarf shrew or Savi's pygmy shrew **Suncus etruscus** *of the Mediterranean, Africa and Malaya. Savi's pygmy shrew has a 1½in. head and body length with a tail 1 in. long. The house shrew is large, with a head and body length of up to 5½ in. It has a long, pointed snout with long whiskers and minute eyes. Its ears are fairly prominent and the tail has longer fur than is usual in shrews and looks very stout. The coat is black to dark brown.*

Spread by man

The house shrew originally lived in the forests of India but, like rats and mice, it has learned to depend on man and has been introduced accidentally to new places, living in and around houses. It has been taken to East Africa and Madagascar in the west and to many islands including New Guinea, Guam and Japan in the east. House shrews reached Guam after the Second World War and have reached Australia in ships but have not become established there.

House shrews are nocturnal, spending the day in burrows or inside houses and warehouses. They emerge at dusk and forage for their natural food of insects and other small animals and their acquired diet of human food and refuse. As they run about they chatter continuously, sounding like coins being jingled together; in China they have been given the name of 'money shrew'

Killing chicks and mice

The success of rats and house mice is mainly due to their liberal diet, for they take advantage of any food made available by man. This also seems to be the reason for the house shrew living with man and becoming spread over a large part of the Old World tropics. As is usual when a wild animal lives with man, it becomes unpopular, and so it is with the house shrew. Although it is beneficial to some extent because it kills insects like cockroaches, it eats meat, bread and other foods and will attack crops like melons, where it digs up the seeds after they have been planted, and also damages stored fruit.

Shrews are renowned for a belligerence out of proportion to their size and the house shrew is no exception. It is disliked by farmers because it kills chicks. The damage it does is probably overestimated and many kills attributed to house shrews are most likely the work of rats. This is because rats kill quickly and silently but the house shrew is not as efficient. It grabs the luckless chick by the leg, works its way up the leg and severs a tendon. The chick is now immobilised and the house shrew can attack its body. Meanwhile the farmer has been alerted by the chick's cheeps and has caught the house shrew red-handed. House shrews also capture house mice, seizing them by the tail and, again, working up to the body and head.

Up to five babies

The house shrew has been studied on Guam where it has been found to breed all the year round. In its native India, it breeds mainly during the monsoon season when food is abundant. Some 2–5 young are born in a nest constructed by both parents, where they stay until they are nearly fully-grown.

Smelly shrews

Apart from stealing food and killing chicks, house shrews are unpopular because of their very strong musky odour which is produced by glands on the sides of the body. It is often said that if a house shrew runs over a bottle of beer or wine the contents are contaminated by the musk. One suggested explanation for this rather incredible story is that the musk clings to the outside of the bottle and is smelt by anyone drinking the contents.

Other shrews also have musk glands but not so well developed as those of the house shrew. The musk does not seem to have a deterrent effect on enemies as shrews are eaten by many predators, and cats will often kill them even if they do not eat them.

The glands are not easy to find as they are hidden by the fur, but can be readily seen on the inside of the pelt if a shrew is skinned. They are especially well developed in males and are variable in females. This suggests a sexual function and it may be that the males leave musky trails behind them which discourage other males from following, so spacing the population. When a female is not in season she also leaves a strong trail, and this discourages any male from following her. When in season she leaves little or no odour which enables the sexes to come together for mating. There would be an obvious economy in such a scheme, but as yet there is no proof that this is so.

A further peculiarity is shared with the white-toothed shrews of Europe. A female with her litter will form what has been called a caravan. The young line up behind the mother. The leading youngster seizes her fur with its teeth and the rest of the litter holds on to the fur of the one in front. Then all run off in step. The musk shrew has been seen to do the same and because of its larger size the caravans it forms are sometimes mistaken for snakes.

class	**Mammalia**
order	**Insectivora**
family	**Soricidae**
genus & species	**Suncus murinus**

Hoverfly

Hoverflies are probably the most skilful of all insect flyers. They can hang suspended in the air then glide rapidly to one side or forwards or backwards, or move up or down to hang suspended once more. They are two-winged flies belonging to the family Syrphidae. Many visit flowers in large numbers to feed on nectar and in America they are also known as flower flies. They are second only to bees in importance as flower pollinators.

Most hoverflies have a superficial resemblance to wasps and bees, being either marked with black and bright colours in contrasting patterns or covered with a coat of short, dense hairs, also variously patterned. In some cases there is such close resemblance between certain species of hoverflies and the wasps and bees living in the same area that there seems no doubt mimicry is involved.

Most of the two-winged flies are unattractive to us, including as they do the mosquitoes and houseflies. Hoverflies are almost all harmless and many are useful as well as being attractive to look at. In Britain the most abundant of them are the little yellow-and-black striped species **Syrphus balteatus** and **S. ribesii**, and the large bee-like **Eristalis tenax**. They are mainly seen towards the end of the summer.

Living helicopters

Hoverflies are most active in sunshine and warm weather. They can be seen in large numbers hovering over flowers with exposed nectaries, and feeding from them. When hovering they sometimes make little rocking movements while accurately maintaining their position. This is a more remarkable feat of controlled flight than it first appears, for the air in which the fly is poised is not motionless. There is almost always some lateral drift or 'wind', as well as eddies caused by rising air currents and the breeze passing around branches and other obstacles. The insect must therefore be constantly making minute adjustments of its wingbeats to avoid being carried up and down or to and fro.

It seems most likely that the hoverfly maintains its position through its sense of sight. Insects' eyes are less efficient than ours at forming images, but much more efficient at detecting small movements. The slightest shift in the fly's position is thus instantly perceived and as quickly corrected, so it remains motionless in relation not to the air around it but to the solid objects within its field of vision. Occasionally it is

Syrphus feeding. Adult hoverflies live entirely on nectar and honeydew which they suck up through their proboscis with its sponge-like tip. This makes them important as flower pollinators, second only to bees, which they also closely resemble with their striking black and yellow markings (10 × lifesize).

slightly displaced and recovery from this is shown in the rocking movements already mentioned.

The eyes of hoverflies are relatively enormous. Other insects with very large eyes, such as the dragonflies and robber flies, need efficient vision to hunt winged prey in the air, but hoverflies feed from flowers and the need for accurate control of their hovering provides the only explanation of their very highly developed sense of sight.

Why do they hover? In a few cases it seems to have some connection with courtship and mating, but in most of them both sexes constantly hover without taking any notice of each other at all. It seems stretching a point to suggest that hoverflies hover because they enjoy doing so, but there is no better explanation at present.

Another curious habit hoverflies have is of continuing to buzz or 'sing' after they have settled and ceased to move their wings. The sound seems to be produced by vibration of the thorax, but why they do this is not known.

Many kinds of larvae

Most hoverflies have a short proboscis that has a sponge-like expanded end with which they mop up sugary liquids. They can feed only on flowers in which the nectaries are exposed, such as those of ivy. Others have a kind of snout which they can push into bell-shaped flowers, and one Oriental genus *Lucastris* has a long proboscis and can feed from tubular flowers. As well as taking nectar, hoverflies also take aphid's honeydew from leaves.

The feeding habits of the adult hoverflies are fairly uniform but those of the larvae are extremely diverse. They may hunt aphids or greenfly, feed on decaying organic matter—often in very foul surroundings, feed on the juices oozing from wounds in trees, burrow into stems or roots of living plants, or feed on the rubbish in the nests of bees, wasps and ants.

The aphid killers include some of the most abundant and familiar hoverflies. Their larvae are slug-like with the body tapering to a kind of neck at the front end. They have no eyes and the head is small and no broader than the neck. They hunt the swarming aphids by touch, crawling among them and swinging the trunk-like neck from side to side. The aphids make no attempt to escape so this method of hunting is very successful. Starting when very tiny with 3−4 aphids a day, a hoverfly larva may be eating 50 or 60 a day when fully grown.

One of the most interesting of the larvae living on decaying matter is that of the drone fly *Eristalis tenax*. The larvae, often called 'rat-tailed maggots', live in the puddles that collect around manure heaps, in water containing little oxygen. At the hind end of its body the rat-tailed maggot has a breathing tube or siphon which is extensible like a telescope. Its length can be adjusted to reach 4 in. to the surface or a small fraction of this when the larva is only just immersed.

Hoverflies that feed on juices from wounded trees do not belong to familiar species and those that burrow into living plants provide exceptions to the rule that hoverflies are harmless. The narcissus fly

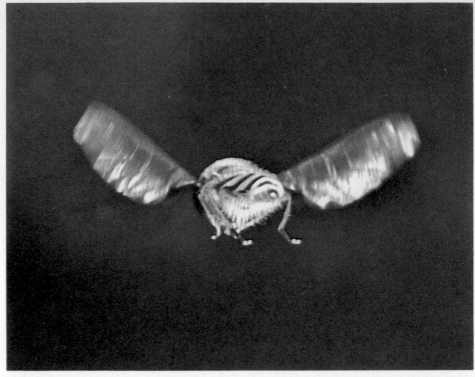

△ **Syrphus luniger** *hovering (8 × lifesize).*
◁ *Rat-tailed maggot—the larva of* **Eristalis** *(1½ × lifesize). The siphon is an extension of the posterior spiracles, an obvious adaptation to life in water or decaying matter. The larva can creep about under water and reach to the air with its extensible breathing tube.*
▽ **Syrphus** *larva—an aphid-eater. The larva raises the front end of its body and swings from side to side until it touches and seizes its victim which is literally a sitting target (7 × lifesize).*
▷ **Volucella zonaria** *is often mistaken for a hornet because of its yellow-banded abdomen. It breeds in wasp and hornet nests (× 16).*

Merodon equestris spends its larval stage inside bulbs of narcissus and daffodil plants, eating their substance and destroying them. In places where bulbs are cultivated on a large scale they may cause considerable losses. The adult fly is large and hairy and looks like a bumble-bee.

Feeding on bees' litter

The big handsome hoverflies of the genus *Volucella* provide the larvae that feed on rubbish in the nests of bees, wasps and ants. The females enter the nests and lay their eggs, and the larvae from them live in the 'rubbish heap' space beneath the nests where dead bee larvae and adult bees are thrown, living on the bodies and any other edible debris. The exact pattern varies according to the type of nest invaded, but in all cases the egg-laying females and the larvae are accepted by the bees and wasps, which are generally most intolerant of trespassers. In the case of the common species *Volucella bombylans*, which usually lays in the nests of bumble bees, the adult flies closely resemble the bees; furthermore the species occur in two distinct forms, each of which looks like a particular species of bumble-bee. It is tempting to think this helps them get into the nests, but this is far from certain, since they also breed in the nests of wasps which they do not at all resemble.

The Samson legend

The resemblance of hoverflies to wasps and bees led to a queer belief that persisted from the dawn of history right up to the 17th century. We meet it in the writings of the classical Latin and Greek scholars and in the Old Testament, in the story of Samson and the lion, and the riddle, 'out of the strong came forth sweetness'.

People believed that a swarm of honeybees could be engendered by leaving the carcase of a large animal to rot. An ox was usually recommended, and in the Samson story it was a lion. The truth is that drone flies *Eristalis* breed in a decaying, liquefying carcase, and after a time large numbers of these bee-like flies emerge from it.

Drone flies have only two wings, bees have four; drone flies do not sting, bees do—and not a drop of honey can ever have been obtained from 'bees' conjured up in this way. In those days, however, all learning was in the hands of classical scholars, and their authority prevailed over any kind of evidence. If Aristotle and Ovid said that carcases produce bees, then the insects that appeared had to be bees. Anyone questioning this would risk his reputation and livelihood, possibly his life.

class	**Insecta**
order	**Diptera**
family	**Syrphidae**
genera & species	*Syrphus balteatus*
	S. ribesii
	Eristalis tenax
	Merodon equestris
	others

Hladik: Jacana

△ An animal alarm clock set for 5 am. The howler monkey begins his lazy day with a good howl, warning others off his territory.
▽ The skull of a male red howler. The thyroid cartilage directs the air to the corniculum which acts as a resonator.

Howler monkey

These, the largest of the South American monkeys, are named for their loud calls. They have enormously enlarged hyoid bones in the throat which form a bony box or resonating chamber, causing a loud voice. The hyoid is smaller in the female than in the male but is still quite remarkable. This bony box makes the neck thick and heavy and the male has shaggy hair around it, making it look even larger. The whole shape of the skull and throat is modified by the vocal apparatus: the lower jaw is expanded at its angle, the skull is long and low. The colour of the fur is usually black, brown or red, but it differs between the five species. The tail is prehensile, with a naked area on the underside at the tip. The hands and feet are large but like other South American monkeys the thumb cannot be opposed to the fingers, so howler monkeys pick up objects with the second and third fingers. Both sexes reach a total length of nearly 4 ft including the tail, but, partly because of the modified neck region, the male is heavier, 16—20 lb as against 12—18 lb in the female.

The range of howler monkeys extends north into southern Mexico and south into northern Argentina, wherever there are tropical and subtropical forests.

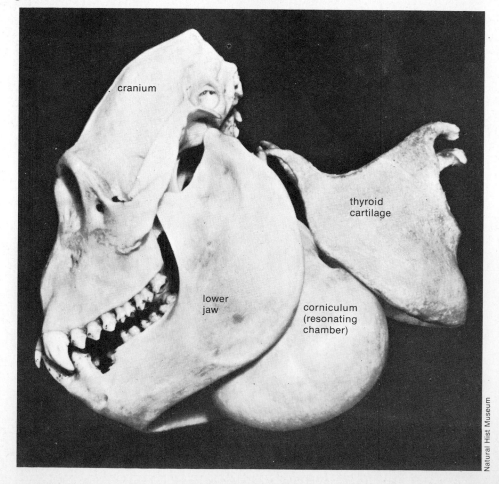

cranium

thyroid cartilage

lower jaw

corniculum (resonating chamber)

Natural Hist Museum

1102

Howling by numbers

When howler monkeys wake at about 5—6 am, most groups begin the characteristic howl, low and resonant in males and a 'terrier-like bark' in females. One group howling stimulates others to do so, and troops usually howl when they catch sight of each other on the edges of the territory or in the 'no-man's-land' between, warning each other against trespassing. After howling, the group begins to feed and laze around in their sleeping-tree. Then, in the middle of the morning, the animals begin to move out to food trees away from the centre of the territory. They rest up until mid-afternoon when they begin to feed again, and they finally travel around and call again before settling down for the night at 7—8 pm.

The daily round

There may be 2—30 howlers in a troop, averaging about 18, in which are 2—3 times as many females as males. Each troop occupies a territory which varies in size according to the amount of food available, so territories change in size and position over the weeks. The troop occupies some areas of the territory more than others, and has favourite sleeping-trees.

Within the group, the males are dominant over the females, but not aggressively so. There is a fairly well-defined dominance hierarchy or 'peck order' among the males, and a less marked and separate hierarchy among the females. The males act in concert in leading the troop and in howling. When the troop meets a neighbouring troop the monkeys act together, the males roaring, females whining, and the young ceasing to play. On rainy days, howlers are less active, and very little roaring can be heard.

Howlers are slow and deliberate in their movements, except when playing and when excited. They never jump from branch to branch, but form a 'bridge', clinging with their prehensile tails and grasping the neighbouring branch with their hands. Often an adult animal lets a youngster use it in this way as a bridge from branch to branch. When moving through the trees the adult males lead the way in order of rank, and all the troop follow exactly the same pathway through the branches.

Wasting their food

Howler monkeys feed on leaves, buds, flowers and fruit. They also eat nuts—shells and all. They are very fond of wild figs which may be one of the reasons for the competition between groups. Each troop needs to have a territory large enough to contain a sufficient number of fig trees. The fruits are pulled in by hand and eaten directly from the stems, but the females sometimes pick and hold food for the young. Strangely, a great deal of the food—as much as half of it—is dropped uneaten, and no effort is made to retrieve it. The prehensile tail is very useful while feeding, wrapped round a branch for stability.

Breeding the year round

At any one time, approximately one third of the females in the troop have infants, which cling to their mothers' bellies, often with the tail wrapped round the base of the

An endearing young male red howler.

AN Warren

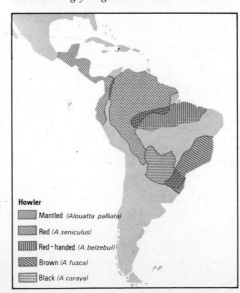

Howler

- ▨ Mantled *(Alouatta palliata)*
- ▨ Red *(A.seniculus)*
- ▥ Red-handed *(A. belzebul)*
- ▨ Brown *(A. fusca)*
- ▤ Black *(A.caraya)*

mother's tail. If the infant becomes separated from its mother it makes a little cry of three notes while the mother makes a wail ending with a grunt or groan. When happy the infants purr. The infant is dependent on its mother for about 6 months, when a second baby is born and the first is rapidly displaced. Most of their time is spent playing—swinging, chasing, wrestling and fooling about.

No serious enemies

Ocelots and other small cats occasionally take young howlers but the adults have no serious enemies. The biggest threat is the clearing of forests in such countries as Brazil, but they are not in danger of extinction as yet.

Howler colonies

Howler monkeys have been intensively studied on Barro Colorado island in Gatun Lake, Panama Canal. The island used to be merely a hilltop, but was isolated when the Chagres River was dammed to supply water for the canal. In 1923 it was made a reservation for the Institute for Research in Tropical America and since 1946 it has been administered by the Smithsonian Institute. In 1933 there were 489 howlers in 28 groups on the island, but in 1949—50 the population suffered a severe reduction, probably as a result of an epidemic of yellow fever. A survey in 1951 showed that there were only 237 individuals left, but these were in 30 troops, so it looks as if there had been a redistribution of individuals between the groups, each of which averaged only 8 animals instead of the usual 18. It is reasonable to expect that an epidemic would bear more heavily on some groups than others, even to virtually wiping some out. Significantly, the males were evenly distributed about each troop. This implies that the howler monkey society is very resilient and can be re-grouped and reorganised when conditions demand.

In 1959, the population had increased to well above its original level when there were 814 individuals in 44 groups. How this has come about is not known. The probable explanation is that a superabundance of food following the epidemic had led to a temporary increase of the population but that in time it will come down again. One further point of interest is that the epidemic bore most heavily on the young. After the epidemic, only 13% of the population consisted of juveniles between 2 and 4 years old, instead of the normal 20%.

class	**Mammalia**
order	**Primates**
family	**Cebidae**
genus & species	***Alouatta palliata*** *mantled or Panamanian howler* **A. seniculus** *red howler* **A. fusca** *brown howler* **A. belzebul** *red-handed howler* **A. caraya** *black howler*

Hummingbird

There are over 300 species of these minute, beautiful birds living in the New World. The largest is the giant humming-bird, a 8½ in. monster compared with the bee hummingbird of Cuba which is little more than 2 in. long; half this length is bill and tail, the body being the same size as a bumblebee. Hummingbirds are very diverse in form, although all of them are small and have the characteristic rapid wingbeats producing the hum that gives them their name. They have brilliant, often iridescent, plumage which has led to their being given names like 'ruby' and 'topaz'—and also to their being killed in thousands and their skins exported to Europe for use in ornaments. A feature of many hummingbirds is the long narrow bill, often straight but sometimes curved, as in the sicklebill. The sword-billed humming-bird has a straight bill as long as the head, body and tail put together.

Hummingbirds are most common in the forests of South America, but they range from southern Alaska to Tierra del Fuego. Some species are so rare that they are known only from collections of humming-birds' skin exported to Europe. Loddige's racket-tail was known from a single skin found in 1840 and was not found alive for another 40 years, when it was dis-covered in a small valley high in the Andes.

Hummingbird stamina . . .

Considering the diversity of habitats and food in the South American forests it is not surprising that there should be so many kinds of hummingbirds living there. It is rather surprising, however, to learn that humming-birds breed as far north as southeast Alaska, or in the heights of the Andes. The rufous hummingbird breeds in Alaska, migrating to South America for the winter, an in-credible journey for so small a bird. The ruby-throated hummingbird also migrates to and from North America, crossing the Gulf of Mexico on each trip. Unlike non-migratory hummingbirds, it stores a layer of fat equal to half its body weight before setting off. At a normal rate of use, however, this would not last through a non-stop crossing of the Gulf. Yet the hummingbirds complete this marathon, so we must pre-sume that they have some method of economising on food reserves.

. . . and speed

Even ignoring the mystery of their migra-tion, the flight of hummingbirds is truly re-markable. Their wings beat so fast they appear as a blur. Small species have wing-beats of 50—80 per second and in court-ship displays even higher rates have been recorded. The fast wingbeats enable the hummingbirds to dart to and fro, jerking to a halt to hover steadily. They are also extremely fast in straight flight—speeds of 71 mph have been recorded. Specialised filming has shown that hummingbirds do not take off by leaping into the air like other

birds but lift off with rapid wingbeats. The photographs showed that a hummingbird on a thin twig actually pulls the twig up as it rises before letting go.

Flying with such rapid wingbeats requires a large amount of energy, so hummingbirds must either feed constantly or have plentiful reserves. Even at rest their metabolism—the rate at which they produce energy—is 25 times faster than a chicken's. At night when they cannot feed they conserve their food reserves by becoming torpid—going into a form of nightly hibernation. In the Andes a hummingbird's temperature drops from 38°C/100°F to 14°C/57°F, about the temperature of the surrounding air—and their metabolism is reduced six times.

Nectar seekers

Hummingbirds feed on nectar and small soft-bodied animals. To sip nectar they hover in front of flowers and insert their pointed bills down the corolla or, if that is too long, pierce it near the base. The nectar is sucked through a tubular tongue that resembles those of flowerpeckers (p 787). Pollen is often brushed onto the humming-birds' heads and transferred to other flowers, so pollinating them. To the flowers of the South American jungle, humming-birds are as important as pollinators as bees are in a clover field. Hummingbirds can readily be attracted to tubes containing sugar-water and they become so tame they will feed at a tube held in the hand.

Small insects are caught on the wing and spiders are taken from their webs. Most hummingbirds are unable to manipulate insects in their bills and have to rush at them so they are forced into the mouth. Some pick insects and spiders from flowers.

Tiny babies

Courtship antics of hummingbirds are difficult to watch as they flit about among dense vegetation too fast for accurate ob-servation. The males fly about in arcs, sing-ing songs that are almost too high-pitched for humans to hear. They are usually promiscuous, mating in the air with several females, but in a few species such as the violet-eared hummingbirds (which have similar plumage for males and females) the male helps rear the family. The nest is a delicate cup of moss, lichen and spiders' webs placed on a twig or amongst foliage. The two eggs are incubated for 2—3 weeks and minute naked chicks hatch out. They are fed by the parent hovering alongside, putting its bill into theirs and pumping out nectar. The chicks grow very rapidly and leave the nest when 3 weeks old.

Hovering skill

When feeding, hummingbirds can be seen hovering steadily and even flying back-wards. They can do this because their wings can swivel in all directions from the shoulder. When hovering the body hangs at an angle of about 45 degrees so the wings are beating backwards and forwards instead of up and down. In each complete beat the wing describes a figure of eight. As it moves for-wards (the downstroke) the wings are tilted so they force air downwards and the bird upwards. At the end of the stroke they

flip over so that the back of the wing is facing downwards and on the upstroke air is again forced downwards. To fly back-wards the wings are tilted slightly so air is forced forwards as well, and the humming-bird is driven back.

The flight of a hummingbird can be com-pared with that of a helicopter with its blades moving in a circle to achieve the same effect of driving air downwards as the hummingbird's wings do by moving back and forth. In the flight of most birds the power is in the downstroke, the up-stroke being merely a recovery phase, but in hummingbirds both strokes are powerful. The breast muscles of a hummingbird weigh a third of its total weight and the muscles drawing the wings upward are half as powerful as those driving the wings down. Non-hovering species have comparatively much smaller muscles for the upstroke.

class	**Aves**
order	**Apodiformes**
family	**Trochilidae**
genera & species	***Archilochus colubris*** *ruby-throated hummingbird* ***Ensifera ensifera*** *sword-billed hummingbird* ***Eutoxeres aquila*** *sickle-billed hummingbird* ***Loddigesia mirabilis*** *Loddige's racket-tail* ***Mellisuga helenae*** *bee hummingbird* ***Patagona gigas*** *giant hummingbird* ***Selasphorus rufus*** *rufous hummingbird, others*

▷ *White-tailed hummingbird feeding.*

Hummingbirds
(family Trochilidae)

'Stones and metals polished by art are not comparable with this gem of nature'. *Buffon*

*The form of individual species of hummingbird is very varied. This male black-throated train-bearer **Lesbia victoriae**, from Ecuador, has long ornamental feathers that do not appear to hinder its aerial acrobatics. Its body is only 2 in. long but the tail is 6 in. with widely forked feathers which help make a marvellous picture when it turns sharply doing its fast manoeuvres in the air. The iridescent throat is absent in the female.*

*Top: Banana-boat feeder. A male velvet-purple coronet **Boissonneaua jardini** greedily sips nectar from **Heliconia jaquinii**, a relative of the bananas. Centre: The white-lipped sicklebill is perfectly adapted for sucking nectar from flowers. Bottom: The tiny ruby-topaz hummingbird **Chrysolampis mosquitus**, a beautiful Brazilian species, vibrates its wings at about 100 beats per second, fast even for the hummingbirds.*

Photos by Walter Scheithauer

Top: The best helicopter bird in action. There is no other bird which can fly so competently when stationary. Although falcons and sunbirds can hover, only the hummingbirds can hold the body quite still in the air. Species: Blue-throated sylph **Aglaicercus kingi**. Bottom: The sword-billed hummingbird **Ensifera ensifera** has an extreme 'pipeline' for flowers with a long tube. The bill measures $4\frac{3}{4}$ in., the body, 3 in.

Skilled construction engineer when it comes to nest design, a ruby-throated hummingbird **Archilochus colubris** feeds its hungry young. The nest is an exquisite cup, less than 2 in. across, made of felted plant, fern or dandelion seed down covered with moss and lichens and fastened with spider webs as to appear a mere protuberance on the twig and lined with a layer of the finest down.

G Rüppeli

R Austing

Humpback whale

The humpback whale belongs to the same family as the better-known whalebone whales but has a number of distinct features that place it in a genus on its own. Its name probably comes from its appearance as it dives, when it arches its back just before disappearing below the surface. Its most characteristic feature is an extremely long set of flippers. Far longer in proportion than in any other whale, they may be as much as one-third of the total body length. The body, far from being streamlined, is barrel-shaped and ugly. Humpbacks migrate a great deal and tend to hug the coastlines as they pass the tropics to waters of high latitudes. Keeping close to the coasts in this way has made their migrations well known but has also made the whales an easy prey for hunters. Humpbacks grow to 40—50 ft in length, the females being slightly

longer. The colour is normally black above and white below, but there are a number of variations on this. The back is fairly constantly all black or a very dark slaty grey, but the amount of white on the underside varies very considerably from almost totally white to nearly all black. Some scientists have tried to divide humpbacks into races on the basis of their colour. This has been found unreliable, although it is probable there is some sort of division, as whalers have noticed that they tend to catch all-dark whales and then all-light whales, as they work through various schools passing along the coast.

The long flippers are usually dark on the upper or outer surface and white on the lower or inner surfaces, and in the same way the tail flukes are dark above and pale below. One female caught off the Shetlands was totally black except for her white flippers. The flippers also have a distinctive outline. The lower margins

are scalloped and they have a number of irregular humps or tubercles along this edge. These tubercles also occur on the upper part of the head and along the jaw line, and each usually has one or two short coarse hairs growing from it.

On the underside are a number of grooves running as far back as the navel. These number 2—36 compared with an average of 85—90 in the fin and blue whales. Each is separated from its neighbour by as much as 8 in. and some-times the concave part of the groove contrasts with the body colour around it. The short dorsal fin is set rather far back and is almost triangular in out-line. It does not have the concave rear edge as in most of the rorquals. There may be as many as 400 baleen plates on each side of the mouth but the average is around 300. They are up to 2 ft in length and greyish black in colour. Sometimes there are a few white baleen plates. When present these are usually at the

front of the mouth and they are often associated with blotchy white markings on the skin in about the same position as the plates themselves.

Cold-warm migrations

Humpbacks are found in all oceans but are typically whales of the coasts, often coming close inshore even into small bays and estuaries. In spite of this they are very rarely found stranded. In this they contrast sharply with false killers (p 735). They migrate every summer to polar waters to feed and back to tropical waters in winter when the young are born and mating takes place. Although there are separate populations in both Arctic and Antarctic waters, by moving towards the Equator in the winter months there is possibly some interchange between the two.

The humpbacks sometimes seen off the British coasts spend the summer with their calves to the north and east of Norway, feeding. In February and March they move westwards and then south as far as the west coast of North Africa where another generation of calves is born and, in April and May, further mating takes place. After this the whales move north again, passing the Outer Hebrides and the Faeroes and finally reaching northern Norway about July or August. Whalers from the Hebrides and Shetland about 60 years ago used to take some humpbacks, but they are seldom seen now, and none has been stranded on British coasts for a very long time. In 1866 one humpback was seen in the Firth of Tay almost daily for a period of about 6 weeks. Eventually it was harpooned and subsequently Sir John Struthers made a detailed description of its anatomy.

The migrations of the southern stocks of humpbacks have been studied in considerable detail, and these follow the same pattern as those in northern waters. The whales spend the summer in the Antarctic feeding on the abundant krill. As the winter approaches they move gradually northwards. The first to go north are the females that have just finished suckling their calves, which go with them. Next are the immature animals, then the mature males and finally the pregnant females. They all go as far as the warm equatorial waters, where the pregnant females give birth and then mate once more. In the return migration the pregnant females go first, followed by immature animals, then the mature males, and finally the adult females with their newly-born calves. By the time they reach the Antarctic feeding grounds the herds have all mixed together and they stay this way until it is time to travel north again.

Krill is the main food

The food of the humpback consists of krill but they do sometimes take small fish and there is one record of a humpback with six cormorants in its stomach and a seventh in its throat. These were probably taken in accidentally when the whale was feeding on the same shoal of krill as the cormorants. Sometimes cod are found in their stomachs. When the humpbacks are in tropical waters they feed very little. Most of the feeding is done in colder waters and the blubber reserves are built up to last through the rest of the year.

Amorous leviathans

Humpbacks are well known for their amorous antics. They will roll over and over in the water, slapping the surface or each other with their long flippers. This causes considerable commotion in the water, and the noise is said to be audible several miles away. Sometimes they leap completely clear of the water in their play, although it has been suggested that this is done to rid themselves of encrusting barnacles.

Killed on the coast

As is the case with many whale species their greatest enemy is man. Killer whales take their usual toll, but the humpback with its coast hugging habits and fixed migratory routes has been an easy prey for man and when a whale fishery has started it is usually the humpback that is killed first.

Barnacle trouble

Humpback whales are usually heavily infested with barnacles and whale lice, one of the barnacles *Coronula* being typically found in association with the tubercles on head and flippers and this barnacle sometimes has a stalked barnacle growing on it. It was long ago noted that humpbacks passing the South African coast on their way north were heavily barnacled, but those returning from tropical waters were only lightly infested. It was believed that when the whales got to where the Congo river emptied into the sea they moved inshore into much less salty water where the barnacles died and dropped off. The story goes that some of the old sailing ship masters would lie in those waters to rid their vessels of barnacles.

Time Life Inc.

class	**Mammalia**
order	**Cetacea**
family	**Balaenidae**
genus & species	*Megaptera nodosa*

*Injecting the poison: a sandwasp **Ammophila** paralyses a huge noctuid moth caterpillar which will be dragged to its burrow and put with other immobilised victims to feed the wasp's larva (about 4 × lifesize).*

Hunting wasp

Wasps can be divided by their habits into social and solitary types. The former are the familiar wasps and 'hornets' which live in colonies or communal nests, may sting severely and often appear very numerous. They are, however, only numerous in terms of individuals; a far greater number of species of wasps are not social insects, but types in which each individual leads an independent life. The hunting wasp is one of these.

Solitary wasps are all, apart from a few exceptions, hunters: the females hunt other insects, spiders and the like and store them in burrows or hollow mud cells, not as food for themselves but as a provision for their larvae. The exceptions are the solitary wasps which have a parasitic or 'cuckoo' mode of breeding, laying their eggs in the burrows of other solitary wasps, or solitary bees. Their larvae then grow by feeding on the store provided by the rightful owner, or by killing and devouring the larvae for which this store was intended. A hunting wasp, then, is a solitary wasp which has not adopted a parasitic mode of life.

Hidden larders

Female hunting wasps spend most of their time providing food and shelter for offspring which, in the great majority of cases, they will never see. These activities follow a fairly uniform pattern.

After mating the female digs a burrow in earth or rotten wood, or seeks out a hollow plant stem, or constructs a receptacle of mud, plastered on while wet and allowed to dry. She then hunts for living insects of some kind, such as caterpillars. When one of these is found it is stung, but the effect of the injected poison is only to paralyse, not to kill it. The caterpillar is then carried to the burrow and put inside, and other caterpillars are sought out, stung and added to the first. When sufficient have been brought to stock one burrow the wasp lays an egg, usually on the wall above the immobilised victims, seals up the burrow and goes on to build and stock similar burrows. After a short time the egg hatches and the hunting wasp larva feeds on the store of living food, sucking the juices of the caterpillars in such a way that they remain alive until almost completely consumed. The residue of skin quickly shrivels and dries and the wasp larva goes on to its next victim. By the time the store of food has been eaten, the larva is ready to turn into a pupa.

Perfect meat store

The provision that the mother wasp makes for her offspring is quite elaborate. She constructs a shelter to protect it from enemies and from extreme temperatures, and she provides a store of food which is kept not merely fresh but alive. There is therefore no danger of the uneaten part of the store putrefying during the development of the wasp larva. On the other hand the tiny,

The potter's larder revealed: the potter wasp **Eumenes** builds a beautifully designed little clay pot and often fastens it, quite high, on plants. Paralysed caterpillars are brought and sealed up after a single egg has been laid which hatches into a larva (above) which devours the caterpillars.

A pupa awaits adulthood: a fully developed potter wasp pupa is ready for the final change, having eaten all the stored paralysed caterpillars during its development. Below: The adult or imago emerges. Unlike its larva, the adult wasp lives mostly on nectar and sap (about 7 × lifesize).

A mud-dauber wasp **Sceliphron** *pushing prey into its nest built from mud as its name suggests. This skilful architect is also noted for its long hind legs and the extremely long 'waist' or stalk of its abdomen (about 6 × lifesize).*

delicate larva cannot be injured by the protesting struggles of its victims, for they are paralysed. (We can only hope they are anaesthetised as well!) Also the wasp provides just enough food for the larva's development, but no excess. If any caterpillars remained after the larva's pupation they would die and putrefy, creating conditions likely to kill the pupa.

Classified by habits

The hunting wasps can be subdivided into two groups, again by reference to their habits: by the prey they hunt and by the sort of nest they make. Hunting wasps do not take their prey indiscriminately; each kind confines itself to a particular type of victim. Also each kind of wasp makes a particular type of nest, and both these features of behaviour are related to the natural classification of the wasps, which is based on careful study of their wings, legs and bodily structure.

Thus members of the genus *Ammophila* dig burrows in sandy soil and stock them with caterpillars. The 'bee killer', *Philanthus*, makes a similar type of nest but stocks it with bees, which it attacks and overcomes easily in spite of their stings. *Gorytes,* another burrower, drags young froghoppers out of their concealing mass of 'cuckoo spit'. The mainly tropical mud dauber wasps *Sceliphron* and allied genera make nests of mud plastered onto any suitable surface, including walls of houses—sometimes, inconveniently, inside the house. They stock their nests variously, but each species is confined to a particular type of prey.

One British wasp makes a clay nest of remarkable beauty. This is the potter wasp *Eumenes,* whose nests look like tiny round flasks, each with a short neck and flared rim. These are stocked with small caterpillars and can be found on heather on dry sandy heaths, although they are less common than they were as heathland habitats are being destroyed.

Victory against heavy odds

The most spectacular of the hunting wasps are the spider hunters of the family Pompilidae. A few small species are found in Britain, including the black-and-red *Pompilus viaticus,* another heath dweller. It hunts

wolf spiders, which might be thought a match for any insect of their own size, but the wasp subdues them and stings them into immobility without any trouble. Some of the tropical pompilids are among the biggest of all wasps and they hunt the huge Mygalid spiders or 'tarantulas'. These formidable creatures, which can kill a mouse with ease, live in burrows, and the wasp will sometimes enter the burrow, where she might be thought to be at a terrible disadvantage. When they fight in the open the two may spar around or they may close and tumble like wrestlers. The wasp's only weapon is her sting, which is pitted against eight clutching legs and a pair of powerful poison fangs—the slender sword of St George against the claws and teeth of the dragon! Almost invariably, however, the wasp is the victor, and manages to slip her sting into the under-surface of the spider, where its nerve centres lie. It has been recorded that some spider hunters deliver the first sting into the spider's head to immobilise its jaws, and then close in to finish the battle.

When large prey of this kind is chosen the wasp has considerable difficulty in carrying it, in fact she may only be able to drag it along the ground. In such cases the usual procedure is for the wasp to find her victim, sting it, and then look for a convenient place nearby to make a burrow. When this is ready the victim is dragged to it, pushed in and an egg is laid. One victim suffices for the larva in these cases!

Wasp watchers

Many people amuse themselves by watching birds, sometimes making valuable observations. But hunting wasps are most rewarding creatures to watch as well. Here are some interesting observations that have been made of them.

The species *Ammophila pubescens,* which lives in sandy places in Europe, departs from the general pattern described here in that the female continues to bring caterpillars to the burrow after the larva has hatched, thus revisiting the nest a number of times during its development. Prof Niko Tinbergen found that an individual of this species may be keeping as many as three dif-

ferent nests going at the same time, all in different stages. In one the egg may not have hatched, in another the larva may need a replenishment of food and a third may be ready for final closure, the larva being ready to pupate. The female wasp has a mental capacity sufficient to enable her to memorise the needs of all three nests at the same time.

Whenever she leaves a burrow she closes it with a plug of earth or sand, making its position practically invisible; yet when she returns to visit it she flies straight to the hidden entrance. The same observer demonstrated ingeniously how she does this. He found a burrow at an early stage and put around it a fairly wide circle of pine cones. On her first return the wasp was put off by this addition to the local scenery, but soon discovered her burrow and from then on flew straight to it. After a few days the observer played a trick on her; he moved the circle of cones a little to one side and watched for the wasp's return. She flew, not to the location of her burrow, but to the centre of the conspicuous circle of cones, clearly showing that she was using them as a landmark. The implication of this is that these wasps always mark their nests by imprinting a picture of its surroundings on their memory.

Another observer claims to have seen an allied species of hunting wasp do a most extraordinary thing. He noted that *Ammophila* always closes her nest when she leaves it. This wasp, in finally closing her burrow, is said to have picked up a very small pebble in her jaws and used it as a hammer to tamp down the plug of sand closing the hole. Cases of animals using tools or instruments of any kind are rare, even among the highly developed vertebrates. In a wasp it is something quite remarkable.

phylum	**Arthropoda**
class	**Insecta**
order	**Hymenoptera**
families & genera	**Pompilidae** *spider hunters* **Vespidae** *Eumenes potter wasps* **Sphecidae** *Ammophila, Gorytes, Sceliphron, Philanthus*

Hutia

Hutias are rodents related to coypus. Most people outside the islands of Central America have never heard of them—but they have a remarkable history. The coypu is South American and the chances are that the ancestors of hutias were also South American. Indeed, there is a Venezuelan hutia **Procapromys geayi** *but only one specimen is known and even this is believed to have been a young individual of the hutia living on the Isle of Pines off Cuba. So this is something of a mystery. Apart from this there were about 20 species, on Cuba, Haiti, Jamaica, Bahamas and other islands lying between North and South America. Of these 20 species most are extinct, having been wiped out during the last few centuries, or had just become extinct when Europeans first reached the New World. The few species still surviving are already becoming rare and are in danger of being wiped out in the foreseeable future.*

Hutias look very like the hyraxes of Africa and both have the local name of coney. They have the blunt muzzle of the coypu and the coarse coat but in most of them the tail is not so long as in the coypu. The four species of hutias on Cuba and the Isle of Pines are up to 18 in. long with a tail 1 ft long, and they weigh up to 15 lb.

Anthony Maynard

Jamaican hutia **Geocapromys brownii** *is rabbit-sized but more stoutly built with short legs and tail. Once common in Jamaica it was an important food for the island's aborigines, but today it is rare.*

No safety in trees

Hutias live in trees, feeding on fruit, leaves, bark, lizards and any other small animals they can find. In the morning especially they bask curled up on leafy branches, looking like clumps of foliage. When in danger they are said to come to the ground seeking safety in holes. The females give birth to 1–3 young after a gestation of 17–18 weeks, the young being born with a reddish-brown fur, which later goes grey; they can run about soon after birth. The hutias of Cuba and the Isle of Pines are hunted with dogs for their flesh. The dogs tree them where they can be caught. They have probably been hunted for a long time as one of the species first became known to scientists from bones found in caves.

Everything against them

The hutias on Jamaica and neighbouring Little Swan Island are slightly smaller than those already mentioned. They live on the broken ground among rugged limestone hills, but even here they are not safe from predators. They are now very rare and the survivors are hunted with dogs. For centuries they have been eaten by the local people and now they are at the mercy of the introduced mongooses as well. They are mainly nocturnal and feed on grass, leaves and fruit, but apart from this little is known about them. Two related species are known, one on Cuba from bones found in caves and one on the Bahamas which became extinct many centuries ago, probably killed off by prehistoric Stone Age hunters.

More extinct than living

There are two species of hutia on Haiti and the Dominican Republic, both very rare, and there are two other species, one known only from bones in kitchen middens—the waste pits of long ago—and the other from bones in caves. They also seem to have been widely used as food for a long time. Two other species on Haiti are known from a few bones only, found in caves, and these must have been extinct when the Spaniards conquered the new Americas. The same can be said of two species on Haiti, the Dominican Republic, Puerto Rico and the Virgin Islands. Their bones are found in middens and in caves and these, like other species, seem to have been preyed upon probably by an extinct giant barn owl as well as being eaten by the local people.

Each island its own species?

Already a picture can be built up of the islands being inhabited by many species of hutias, different species in different areas of the Caribbean, probably all descended from coypu-like ancestors from South America. They were probably very numerous thousands of years ago, with the giant barn owl their only enemy until man arrived. As the hutias grew rare, hunted by primitive man, the giant barn owl probably died out and now the hutias look like dying out, killed first by man for food, and now by imported mongooses as well as introduced rats. And every few years the bones of yet another extinct species of hutia are found, showing that formerly these animals existed in many more species than the score already known.

The West Indies have been the scene of several notable introductions of animals, most of them without thought about the effect. Many of these have disturbed if not destroyed some of the local animals. Examples are the common rat, the mongoose, as well as domestic cats and dogs. There is one, however, worth recalling here, especially as it is harmless. This is the flourishing colony of the greater bird of paradise established on Little Tobago in 1909 by Sir William Ingram (see p 202).

Contrast from Africa

On the other side of the Atlantic, in West Africa, lives the cutting grass or grass-cutter, also known as the cane rat and, to the Africans, as the oya. It is a near relative of the hutias but its story is the reverse of theirs. Up to 2 ft long and 16 lb in weight, the cutting grass looks very like a coypu, swims well and lives near damp ground but it does not burrow although it has been found at times in termites' nests. It lives in family groups and feeds at night especially on young plants, and particularly on grasses. The female may have three litters a year each with up to six babies, in a nest of weeds in a depression in the ground usually concealed in a thicket.

The cutting grass is a pest for which control measures are being sought. Nearly 95% of damage to crops in Sierra Leone, Nigeria and other parts of Africa are due to it. Crops which suffer are maize, rice, young oil palms, sweet potato, cassava and sugar cane, all being attacked when half grown. The Africans used to hunt it for food, beating it into nets but with the industrialization of parts of Africa the local peoples are less inclined to do this. Putting down poison has proved useless as the cutting grass is almost solely attracted by young green plants—not by grain or meal, the most convenient poison bait.

If a ready means could be found of catching the cutting grass—without poisoning it—this would prove a profitable source of animal protein and would preserve the 20–30% of the rice crop at present being eaten by this rodent.

class	**Mammalia**
order	**Rodentia**
family	**Capromyidae**
genera & species	***Capromys pilorides*** Cuba ***C. prehensilis*** Cuba ***Plagiodontia aedium*** Haiti ***P. hylaeum*** Haiti ***Thryonomys swinderianus*** cutting grass

Hyaena

There are three species of hyaena: the spotted or laughing hyaena of Africa south of the Sahara, the brown hyaena of southern Africa and the striped hyaena which ranges from northern and northeast Africa through Asia Minor to India. They all have massive heads and powerful jaws and teeth with which they can crack even marrow bones. Their ears are large and their shoulders are markedly higher than their hindquarters. Their tails are short and each foot has four toes. The male spotted hyaena may be 5 ft long, head and body, with a 13 in. long tail, and 36 in. high at the shoulders, and can weigh up to 180 lb. The female is slightly smaller. The hyaena's coat is grey to tawny or yellowish-buff with numerous brown spots. There is only a slight mane.

Norman Myers

AJ Sutcliffe

A scavenger's life

The spotted hyaena is a nocturnal animal spending most of the day in a hole in the ground (above) or in a cave or lair in dense vegetation. It is very difficult to tell apart the sexes of this species as both have similar external reproductive organs. A myth has grown up that each hyaena may act as male and female. The gestation period is 110 days after which one or two young are born fully furred. Inside the lair of a spotted hyaena (left) are the spoils of a scavenger. The bones include the lower jaw of a cow and the top of a human skull carried away from a cemetery.

Norman Myers

Okapia

Maxlenz: WWF

The largest and most aggressive of the three species of hyaena is the spotted hyaena and unlike the other two it does not limit its diet to carrion and small prey. But it is cowardly and will not fight if a victim defends itself. It may also feed on the kill of bolder carnivores, forming a pack and rushing on a lion which is enjoying a good meal. The lion is usually driven away in frustration leaving his well-earned meal to the scavengers. When eating carrion such as that of gnu (below left) the hyaena crushes the long bones with its strong teeth and powerful jaws eating all he can of the victim. The sorry remains of a meal are being carried away by a spotted hyaena (below centre) probably to the lair for the offspring.

The three species of hyaena are easily recognised by their coats. That of the brown hyaena (above) is dark brown with greyish neck and lower legs. The coat is exceptionally long and heavy. Both the brown and striped hyaenas (below right) have long haired manes which can be erected. The striped hyaena has a grey to yellowish-brown coat with brown or black stripes. It has strong fore-paws which are well adapted for digging up meat from caches made by other carnivores. The spotted hyaena (right) has a yellowish-grey coat with many brown or black spots. It has no long mane and has shorter ears. Its jaws are probably the most powerful in proportion to size of any living mammal.

Norman Myers

Okapia

Vultures and a jackal keep a respectful distance while hyaenas take their fill from a zebra carcase.

Spotted hyaena clans

Spotted hyaenas spend most of the day in holes in the ground, in caves or in lairs in dense vegetation. Although typically nocturnal they are sometimes active by day. They live in clans of up to 100 at times, in defined territories marked by their urine and droppings. Members of other clans are driven from the boundaries. They often hunt in packs, can run up to 40 mph and are more aggressive than the other two species. The voice of the spotted hyaena is a howl, made with the head held near the ground, beginning low but becoming louder as the pitch rises. When excited, as during the breeding season, it makes its so-called laugh. The spotted hyaena has also been credited with imitating a man's voice, even with calling men by name—a belief that goes back to the Middle Ages.

Spotted hyaenas eat carrion, crushing the long bones of large animals such as buffalo. They also kill sheep, goats, calves, young antelopes and even smaller prey. They may eat even locusts. Immensely strong in the jaws and shoulders they are said to be able to carry away a human body or the carcase of an ass.

There has long been a legend (quite false) that hyaenas are hermaphrodite because the external reproductive organs are superficially similar in both sexes. One or two young are born after a gestation of 110 days. At the birth the mother takes up a squatting position and the young, born fully furred, are ejected forwards. The life span is up to 25 years.

Striped and brown hyaenas

The striped hyaena is usually smaller than the spotted species, being not more than 4 ft head and body with an 18 in. tail. It stands 30 in. at the shoulder and weighs up to 85 lb. The coat is grey to yellowish-brown with blackish stripes and a mane or crest of long hairs. The diet is like that of the spotted hyaena. Its breeding differs from the spotted hyaena in that the gestation period is 90 days and there are 2−4 in the litter, sometimes 6. Otherwise it is much the same. The babies are born in holes in the ground, blind and with their ears closed.

The brown hyaena is halfway in size between the spotted and striped hyaenas. Its coat is dark brown with indistinct stripes but with dark rings round the lower legs. Its breeding and feeding habits are like those of the striped hyaena, but it lives near the shore and feeds on carrion left by the receding tide, eating anything from dead crabs to the carcases of stranded whales. For this reason it is also known as the strandwolf.

The striped hyaena has given rise to all manner of beliefs about its magical powers and its cunning. One thing that led to such ideas is its habit at times of shamming dead when cornered by dogs. The hyaena lies perfectly still and the dogs, having sniffed around it for a while, lose interest and begin to turn away. At that moment the hyaena jumps to its feet and dashes away—at 40 mph!

Not so cowardly

Another belief that has persisted to this day is that hyaenas are cowardly and live by feeding on the remains of the lion's kill. This has now been finally disproved. Already there had been cause to doubt this when Dr Hans Kruuk, of the Serengeti Research Institute in Arusha, Tanzania, made a close study of hyaenas by following them on moonlit nights in a Land-Rover. He found that at dusk they came out of their holes, often crevasses in the mud, to walk about slowly, meeting other hyaenas, ex-changing greeting ceremonies until a pack of up to 20 was formed. Then they set off, closely bunched or spread out, in a seemingly leisurely way until a family party of zebras or a herd of wildebeest was reached. Then they began to harass their quarry, snapping at them until they had slowed one down, when all the hyaenas concentrated on it. By dawn not even a splinter of bone would be left. Kruuk found that hyaenas are scavengers but at night they go out to kill for themselves, and the belief in their cowardly disposition is unfounded.

In fact, Kruuk found that as often as not it was the lions that partook of the hyaenas' kills, instead of the other way round.

class	**Mammalia**
order	**Carnivora**
family	**Hyaenidae**
genera & species	***Crocuta crocuta*** spotted hyaena ***Hyaena brunnea*** brown hyaena ***H. hyaena*** striped hyaena

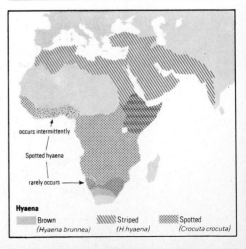

occurs intermittently

Spotted hyaena

rarely occurs →

Hyaena

■ Brown
(Hyaena brunnea) ▨ Striped
(H.hyaena) ▨ Spotted
(Crocuta crocuta)